A Fresh Northerly

New Writings from Sutherland and Wester Ross

First published in 2006
by Northwest Highland Writers
and Sutherland Writers
All rights reserved

ISBN: 0-9552505-0-1
         978-0-9552505-0-7

Cover design by Charlie Byron
Produced by Big Sky, Findhorn.
Printed on 75% post-consumer waste recycled paper

Acknowledgements

We would like to thank the following people and organisations: the late
James Henderson for his enthusiastic support and advice; the Highland
Council's Community Events Fund; Awards for All; Big Lottery Fund;
and Tom Bryan for his editorial advice.

Contents

Foreword

The prevailing winds in Scotland may be westerlies, but if these pages are anything to go by, a fresh northerly is the wind to wish for. Twenty-five East Sutherland and Northwest writers are showcased here, as pleasant a crew as could ever have been drawn from the chiselled land that sweeps from Golspie to Lochinver, from Ullapool to Durness. The briefest glance at the list of contributors confirms their flexibility and diversity – native highlanders, lucky enough to have been born in this country of mountain and moor, rubbing shoulders with newer (no less committed) highlanders, seduced by landscape and the warmth of northerly community, from London, Manchester, Glasgow, California, Liverpool.

They are concerned, as you might expect, with the land and its history. They are concerned with humanity, with love and death and loss with humour and hope. They are not afraid to challenge out-dated orthodoxies. They are confident in their reading of the world, and in their writing of it.

Northerliness has always been fashionable – take the detective fiction of Henning Mankell or the great Cape Breton writer Alasdair Macleod, or Peter Høeg's *Miss Smilla's Feeling for Snow* – the mystery of the North, its wheeling light and dark, entrances. These stories and poems add to the genre, a snapshot of the North and West here and now. *A Fresh Northerly* is, as the title implies, a stream of ideas, of stories, at once bracing and beguiling. Northwest Highland and East Sutherland Writers are to be congratulated on their sense of North.

Anne MacLeod

Unrequited

Jackie Aris

I am a fool at heart I know,
For when those eyes I see,
That penetrate my very soul
Yet see so little of me,
I think I've found a lasting love
And once again I am blind,
I look to see what I want to see
With my intense and fickle mind.
I sigh a sigh,
I thought this one was different from the rest.
His handsome face and rugged charm,
Those twinkling eyes could quite disarm.
Yet when I've satiated myself to rest
Dreams made reality,
My lover cannot stand the test
I need once more to be free.
My thoughts of this one
Who would be *the* one,
Are once more dashed and drowned,
For once I have what I sought to hold
I throw it to the ground.
The only love I will ever keep
Will be the very best:
Love unrequited, though uninvited,
Will outstay all the rest.

Frosted Fodder

Mary Black

Hoary hills and hedges,
Sugar-sifted fields,
Gloomy Galloways chew on
Crisp grasses.
Does it cut their tongues?
Do the icy blades make their
Teeth ache?

Happy Birthday

Mary Black

Becky tied her garters, securing her striped stockings as best as she could. Next came the cage and three petticoats. The final layer was a green brocade overskirt. Kate, her maid, pulled, pinched and tucked to no avail. The dress was too wide and too long. In desperation she tied a broad sash, cummerbund fashion, around Becky's waist and stepped back to examine the result. Her mistress looked like a child dressed up in her mother's clothes. In fact they were her sister's.

The dress should have been Lucy's wedding gown but Lucy had rebelled against marrying their stepmother's uncle. He was their neighbour, the Laird of Broomlands, which was only one of his many estates. Uncle Fergus also owned property in Glasgow, where his money came from tobacco, and in London where he had investments in shipping.

Becky's father Alex had beaten Lucy for her refusal to cooperate in his plan to bring a share of this fortune into his own pocket. He locked her in her room from which she escaped by climbing down a vine, and she ran off with her lover, a penniless Major.

Alex and his wife Marjory had proposed Becky as a substitute but old Fergus Gilchrist had looked with distaste at the scrawny fifteen -year-old and declined even though he knew his time was running out. His doctor had warned him to set his affairs in order.

Becky was wearing the outfit for the party to celebrate her sixteenth birthday. As father had said, they could not afford to waste it. She looked at her reflection in the glass. "I look as if I have grown out of a hedge like some weird piece of topiary", she said to Kate who remained silent but was inwardly in agreement.The enormous crinoline did indeed resemble a piece of shrubbery.

Kate tweeked at the curls of a tall elaborate wig.

"I am not wearing that moth-eaten monstrosity", Becky told her. "It has been in that cupboard since the Bonnie Prince was a bairn and I'm not having powder on my head either. It makes me sneeze as well as looking stupid." Kate was happy to agree. Becky's glossy brown hair was her best feature. She arranged it on top of her head. It was the first time she'd had her hair up and the style suited her. Her eyes looked bigger and her face more patrician. There was a hint of the elegant woman she would become.

"You are the image of your dear mother as she was at sixteen ",

Kate said with a tear in her eye. "She had yet to grow into her looks, and she did, as you will too."

"I wish Lucy was here," Becky sighed.

"Hush lassie. We've not to mention her name. This is your day. Try to enjoy it."

"But they haven't invited one of my friends, Kate, not one. It is all old people who are waiting down there."

Her elderly guests greeted her with birthday salutations and many compliments on her looks. Her father poured her a glass of wine. "Drink up, my dear," he said. "A young lady must learn to recognise a good vintage." It was her first taste of alcohol and she happily obliged, feeling more and more sophisticated with every sip.

She was surprised to see Fergus Gilchrist among the guests. She had thought that he would never set foot in this house again after the way Lucy had humiliated him. She had been cruelly vociferous in her rejection. Becky could easily see why an eighteen-year-old girl would not want to marry such a mean-eyed unattractive old man; he was at least fifty years her senior, but she could have been more diplomatic. Becky felt quite sorry for him and smiled at him in wine-enhanced pity. It was not just her feelings that were wine-enhanced. Her eyes sparkled and her cheeks flushed prettily. As she turned away she did not see the sudden spark of interest come to life in the old man's eyes.

"She is not as comely as Lucy," he said to Alex. "But she has improved since I saw her last and her manners are nicer."

"True," Alex replied. "And she is of good stock. My first wife was very well-born."

"So was your second," snapped Fergus in a sharp reminder of his relationship to the lady.

"Oh, of course, of course," muttered Alex, a plan beginning to form in his head.

After dinner they began to play charades and other games that required some acting.

Becky played her parts well with alcohol-induced courage. She was Joan of Arc and then a splendid Queen Mary at her wedding, at which point things began to become hazy. Alex had given her a pill that was supposed to help her get over the wine but it was making her sleepy.

The next morning she awakened slowly and painfully and very much against her will. Her head was pounding and her eyes were glued shut. She felt depressed and uneasy and tried to escape from it by attempting to fall back into sleep but she could not. The bed felt gritty and lumpy and there was an unpleasant sort of medicinal smell in the stale atmosphere. It was no good. She would have to get up and get washed and dressed before she would feel any better.

"Eyes open! Limbs move!", her thoughts commanded. She used her fingers to prise her lids apart, while uttering the immortal words "I'll never take strong drink again". She struggled to focus on an unfamiliar canopy above her head and spoke that other timeless phrase, "Where am I?" Her unease turned to dreadful foreboding as awareness impinged on her consciousness.

She forced her head to turn on the pillow. Two malicious eyes regarded her through the heavily draped gloom. Goose-pimples prickled from her scalp to her toes. Next to her lay a wizened yellow gargoyle.

"So come and give your husband a kiss, then," it said leeringly.

She closed her eyes and prayed, "I want to wake up now, please." Nothing changed. "I want to go home now," she moaned.

"You are home, wife." He leaned over and squeezed her small breast, then pulled her hand between his wrinkled papery thighs.

"Oh, yeugh," she screamed. "My father will horsewhip you when I tell him about this."

"You are no longer the concern of your father. You are my chattel now, Lady Gilchrist, and I promised him a pretty penny for you, so you can start earning it. I need an heir so that my ungrateful poltroon of a nephew won't inherit the estates which are entailed, so you had better start behaving like a wife. He won't get my money or businesses. I sorted all that out with my man while you were still snoring."

She sat up on her knees, saying "I don't know how to be a wife and I don't want to. Nobody asked me if I wanted to be married. I don't. I'm too young."

"Of course nobody asked you what you want. What a stupid notion. Lasses do what they are bid by their father and then their husband. Now do your duty." He pulled her to him, again trying to pull up her nightgown. The feel of his gnarled hands on her body made her frantic with fear although she could not have said what she was afraid of. She struggled on to her knees again and this time he clipped her sharply on the nose with his knuckle. He must have hit a blood vessel because she bled on her lap and the sheet.

At last she scrambled free of him and looked around the room for her clothing. There was nothing but a dressing gown, obviously his. She pulled it on. She glanced at the bed to see that he had fallen asleep again. The struggle must have exhausted him. She cleaned her face and bloody nose with cold water from a ewer. Fortunately there was no swelling or bruising. She went closer to the bed to make sure that he was still asleep and realised that he was lying at a strange angle, his eyes were still open and his skin had taken on a bluish tinge.

In her sixteen years she had never witnessed death, not even her mother's, but now suddenly she recognised it. She pulled on the bell rope and ran into the hall, shouting for help. She wondered what would happen now. Would they blame her? Had she caused his death by fighting with him?

The butler took control of the situation and the housekeeper took Becky under her wing. There were no signs of grief from the servants. Fergus had not been a popular master.

The housekeeper, who was called Mrs McEwan, helped Becky back into the green dress which she had found in the room next door. "I'll attend to this," she said, picking up the stained nightgown.

"No, just burn it please. I never want to see the horrid thing again," Becky said.

She was still a bit hysterical as people began to arrive.

In the drawing room she was introduced to the minister, the doctor and the solicitor.

"I'm sorry," she kept telling anyone who would listen. "I think it was my fault. I got him too excited."

The minister looked embarrassed but the doctor was sympathetic. "He had a stroke, my dear. I've been warning him for ages not to overdo things, but he was thrawn, so he was the one at fault."

The solicitor said he had some embarrassing questions that he was obliged to ask to do with the consummation and therefore the legality of the marriage. He called in Mrs McEwan to keep her company. She brought the stained nightgown with her.

"Mrs McEwan!" said Becky in a shocked voice. "Whatever are you thinking of to bring that disgusting thing in here? I told you to burn it."

"Now, now, Lady Gilchrist," solicitor Swan said. "She was quite right to let us see it. It is evidence in support of your claim, as are the sheets on the marriage bed, which we three have witnessed and will attest to."

Becky's face radiated heat, a fact that was noted by each of the people present as a sign that all was as it should be.

"Tell me, Lady Gilchrist," Mr Swan continued. "Just how did the blood come to be on the sheets?"

"Mr Swan!", Mrs McEwan felt compelled to interject. "She is but a child!"

"I'm aware of that, but the law requires certain proofs and I must ask. Did the laird do something of an intimate nature to you?"

Becky recalled his hands on her body and how he had tried to make her touch him. She cringed and answered "Yes".

"Was it something he did that caused you to bleed?" "Yes", she said and burst into tears.

"Enough, man," said the Reverend McPherson. "I am convinced as I am sure the good doctor is." The doctor nodded.

"Make your report and we will ratify it. Mr and Mrs McEwan can act as witnesses."

"Very well," said Mr Swan, relieved to have the business behind him. "I can now tell you that you are an extremely wealthy young woman. His Lordship's nephew was killed in a riding accident and apart from some small bequests to servants and his niece, your stepmother, you are the sole heir. So concerned was he that neither his nephew nor your father would get their hands on his property that he made stipulations that you have full control of your affairs with some guidance from me. Would you care for me to send for your parents?"

"Absolutely not," she replied cheerfully.

Easter Eggs

Sharon Blackie

Isobel twitched impatiently as she watched Clarence turn a wary eye on Archie and step smartly in front of Hattie, guarding her with his body.

'Ahem. Er – see here, Clarence. This really won't do, old chap.' Archie threw what was clearly intended to be a winning smile in Clarence's direction. Isobel sighed. Clarence glared. Archie paused for a moment, cleared his throat and scratched his head, dislodging a few wood shavings that had settled on his shoulders like monstrous flakes of dandruff. 'Er – come on, old boy. Please?' Clarence was unmoved. Isobel fidgeted. 'Mixed corn,' Archie said hopefully. 'Mashed potato and mushy peas. Your favourite.'

One leg lifted; long toes splayed and then slowly curled inwards. Clarence looked off to one side as if quite unconcerned by the turn events had taken. Only the intense concentration reflected in the quivering of his tail feathers caused Isobel to doubt the apparently casual pose.

'Archie, I really do think –'

'Ahem, Isobel. Please. Clarence and I are having a man-to-man chat.'

Isobel rolled her eyes, tapped a foot and bit down on her frustration.

Archie turned back to Clarence, who took one step forward and half-opened his beak in a decidedly sinister fashion. Archie twitched.

'Ah, well. Ah, now … Come on, Clarence, old thing… This really won't do, you know …'

Oh, for God's sake, Isobel thought as she watched Archie reach out tentatively towards the nest where Hattie sat tightly, apparently quite oblivious to the spectacle that was unfolding before her. Clarence, pushed to his limit, leapt into action and attacked the back of Archie's right hand. Archie yelped. Clarence cackled and flapped his wings. Hattie sank down even lower on the clutch of pale brown eggs that she was determined to hatch. She had the vacant, dreamy look in her eyes that descended upon females of all species whenever they thought about babies.

Isobel saw red. She stalked over and shoved Archie to one side. Sensing victory in the forced retreat of his enemy, Clarence threw his head back and puffed himself up to utter a crow that turned rapidly into an outraged squawk as Isobel whirled around, grasped him by both legs, deposited him outside, and closed the barn door behind her.

'Sorry, Hattie,' Isobel said in a hard voice. 'Those eggs are promised to Mrs Mackenzie. There's no time for all this broody nonsense.' She tightened her lips, and in one fluid movement scooped Hattie out of the nest and began to place the eggs carefully into a dark wicker basket. She turned to leave and almost fell over Archie, who was sitting in a heap of manure-coated wood chips, scratching his head and clearing his throat obsessively. 'Oh, for God's SAKE,' she said. 'Pull yourself together, Archie. It's only a bloody chicken.'

Caught in the clutches of a restless sleep, Isobel dreamed that she had gone into the pantry to fetch the basket of pale brown eggs. But when she looked down at the basket in her hand, she saw that they'd hatched into perfect little replicas of herself, as if each egg had contained the potential for the daughters that she'd never been able to have, mocking the barrenness of the eggs she held inside her own body – eggs that were destined to remain unfertilised. Clutching the basket, she turned to leave the pantry but Archie barred the way, the slump of his shoulders matching the bleak look of failure in his eyes.

Archie sniffed hopefully as he opened the door to the kitchen, but there was no answering aroma from the range. Ah well, he sighed to himself: looked like it was cornflakes again this morning. Didn't she know it was Easter Sunday? Surely that was worth a rasher or two.

Isobel sat at the table, looking out across the field to the sombre grey glitter of the loch. She looked tired. The weight of his own helplessness sank heavily down in Archie's chest. He took a deep breath, and fixed a cheery grin on his face.

'Morning, darling,' he boomed, rather more loudly than he'd intended.

Isobel flinched, then turned her head and managed a half-hearted smile. 'Morning.'

'Happy Easter.'

She blinked at him vaguely. 'Easter. Oh yes. I'd forgotten about Easter.'

Archie's determinedly jolly smile slipped. If they'd been able to have children she wouldn't have been able to forget. There would have been hard-boiled eggs to decorate and Easter eggs to bury and hunts to organise; he remembered it all so vividly from his own childhood. But never mind: this year he'd taken matters into his own hands. After all, you didn't have to have children to enjoy Easter. He broke into a soft but spirited rendition of 'Easter Bonnet' and crossed over to the huge oak dresser, from the depths of which he extracted a brightly wrapped, much beribboned parcel. He carried it carefully over to the table and placed it with a flourish in front of her. She looked at him blankly.

'For you,' he said proudly.

With limited enthusiasm but an effort at good cheer she tore off the paper. There before her – wrapped in gold-tinted plastic, emblazoned with red bows, resplendent with flowers of pink and blue candy, and sporting a soft, fluffy, but definitely smirking Easter bunny – sat a giant chocolate egg.

Isobel uttered a choked cry, smashed the egg with her fist and ran from the room.

Archie stared after her, his mouth open and an expression of utter bewilderment on his face.

Isobel finally gave up trying to sleep at midnight. She slipped out of bed, shivering in the cool night air. Archie snorted and groaned as he rolled into the warm hollow she'd just vacated. She pulled her old towelling bathrobe over her flannel pyjamas, crept to the window and drew back the curtain. She caught her breath. The sky arched overhead like a tented ceiling hung in subtly varying shades of dark blue velvet, and a full moon shone silver on the surface of the loch. Everything was quiet, and perfectly still.

Down on the shore, something moved. A flash of white skin, the glitter of glassy eyes that mirrored the moonlight. Isobel moved closer to the window and peered out. A small creature sat slender and motionless on the beach, small whiskered nose turned up to the sky and long pointed ears flat against its neck. With a sudden sharp turn of its head, the distance between them shrank into nothingness and Isobel could have sworn that it winked.

She crept down the stairs and into the boot room, slid on her shoes and slipped her brown tweed overcoat over her nightclothes. An owl in the wood hooted its nightly omens to an oblivious world as she stole through the door like a shadow.

Archie woke to the sound of pans crashing on the Rayburn and crept hopefully down to the kitchen. He opened the door and the smoky smell of crisply grilled bacon assaulted his nostrils. Isobel turned from the kitchen counter, auburn hair free and loose around her face, and beamed at him brightly.

'Eggs and bacon, darling?'

His jaw dropped. 'Er – yes. Yes, indeed. Eggs and bacon would be just the thing. Thank you, darling. Ahem. Yes.'

Hardly able to believe his luck, Archie slipped into a chair at the kitchen table. He blinked owlishly as Isobel danced over with a steaming cup of freshly percolated coffee.

'You, er – well, I say, you seem very cheerful, darling.'

'Yes, darling, I do, don't I?'

Archie smiled up at her helplessly. He really didn't understand Isobel; not now, and not on the day they'd met – ten years ago now – at the party his flatmates had insisted on throwing after their final exams. She had burst into the room at midnight like a blazing red star, and he'd followed her slavishly with his eyes. She had stroked his floppy brown hair back from his forehead and called him 'alone and palely loitering'. At the time he'd had no idea what she meant, though in retrospect he wondered if perhaps it had something to do with the fact that he'd been feeling a bit nauseous after one too many glasses of Tony's rum punch. It had temporarily deprived him of the use of his legs and the capacity for intelligible speech. He had been perplexed, but smitten. He suspected that he'd turned out to be a bit of a disappointment to her, but when Isobel got an idea into her head there was little short of an earthquake that could shift it. So they'd been married within six months, and everything had gone really quite smoothly until they'd decided to try for a baby. He sighed. That was when everything had begun to go wrong.

He watched in bemusement as she sailed breezily around the kitchen and finally placed before him an enormous platter of fried egg, bacon, tomato and mushrooms. She sashayed back to the counter and popped bread into the toaster; she swayed from side to side to the jaunty rhythm of Bill Withers's 'Lovely Day', which trumpeted from the radio like a promise of good things to come. Entranced, Archie followed her with his eyes and the forkful of food that he had been conveying to his mouth missed completely, smearing bright yellow egg yolk all over his jaw.

Archie whistled tunelessly as he entered the barn, basket in hand. He didn't know where Isobel had got to, so he had thought he'd just collect the eggs and put the chickens to bed to save her the job. Do something nice for her to make up for the damned fine breakfast she'd produced that morning. As he headed for the nest boxes at the back of the barn he noticed to his surprise that the broody coop had been set up in the corner. He bent down and peeked in. Yes, there was a hen in there, and as far as he could tell in the shadowy gloom it appeared to be Hattie. He raised an eyebrow and shook his head; Isobel had obviously had a change of heart. She really had been in a much better mood today: almost like her old self, in fact. He blushed to remember the afternoon's activities; he wasn't sure the antique satin eiderdown on their bed would ever fully recover. It had been a long, long time.

He moved in closer to check on the contents of the food and water containers inside the small mesh run, when something in the nest box caught his eye. He peered into the nest box where Hattie sat, flat and still. And blinked. Because bulging out from under Hattie's right wing was something that looked suspiciously like a large green egg. A seriously large green egg. Archie closed his eyes and shook his head vigorously, but when he opened them again it was still there. And what's more, the egg – if that's what it was – appeared to be emitting a faint green glow. He reached out a hand to open the run, when the hairs on the back of his neck began to prickle. He whipped his head around to look behind, somewhat unbalancing himself in the process. Isobel loomed over him with an odd little gleam in her eyes.

Archie let out a small shriek and then snickered in embarrassment. 'Ah … hello, darling. You startled me.'

She smiled enigmatically.

'I … er … I just came down to collect the eggs.' He cleared his throat nervously. Not that he had anything to be nervous about, of course. 'You decided to let Hattie sit, after all?'

Isobel shrugged. 'She was so determined. It seemed a pity not to let her.'

'Well, that's wonderful, darling. How lovely for Hattie. But …', he trailed off uncertainly, glancing back at the nest box. 'There seems to be a rather … unusual egg there.'

'Nonsense, Archie. Whatever are you talking about?' The smile was wider now.

'Really, darling. I caught a glimpse of it just now. It's far too big for a hen's egg. Bigger than a goose egg. It's enormous. And it's green.'

'Green?' Isobel lifted an eyebrow. 'Any particular shade of green?'

Archie thought for a moment. 'A sort of pistachio green, it seemed to me.' Isobel smirked, and Archie felt himself blush. 'No, really, Izzie. I'll show you.' He turned back to the door of the run, but Isobel reached out and clamped a surprisingly firm hand on his shoulder.

'Archie, darling. You're imagining things. And anyway: I think it's best if you just leave the hens to me, in future. You have quite enough to do around the estate as it is.' Firmly, she extracted the basket from his hand. 'Why don't you go back to the house and put the kettle on?'

For a moment Archie thought of persisting, but an image of today's breakfast flashed into his mind, rapidly followed by yesterday's solitary bowl of cornflakes. He closed the mouth that he had begun to open, and glanced down at his watch.

'Too late for tea. Just about time for a cocktail before dinner, don't you think?'

Isobel produced her enigmatic little smile again. 'Oh, I don't think so. I don't think I shall be drinking alcohol for a while.'

A few weeks later, looking for Isobel, Archie peered into the barn. She sat cross-legged on the floor in front of the broody coop in which Hattie still appeared to be resident. She was humming a lullaby; her hands rested on the gentle, barely perceptible swell of her own abdomen. Silently, hopefully, he crept away.

On the two hundred and seventieth day after Easter Sunday, the glowing green egg finally hatched. Isobel watched as it cracked open, and out popped a perfectly formed baby hare with a pure white coat and green glowing eyes. She opened the door of the run; Hattie squawked plaintively as it ran through the barn door and out towards the loch. Isobel smiled and clutched at her belly as her waters broke and the warm liquid seeped through the straw and down into the soft brown earth.

The baby was born later that afternoon.

Speechless, Archie looked down at his daughter. She looked so delicate with her lily white skin and the strangely thick pelt of white-blonde hair that covered her scalp and dusted the tips of her long, slightly pointed ears. He reached for her tiny fist, and smiled down into a pair of unblinking pistachio green eyes.

Rock

Irene Brandt

The life span of man is meaningless, relative to geological time. The Earth has her own time-scale and rocks are her children. They are born, and breathe, and move to an aeonic pace and they, too, will eventually die. Who knows what lumbering thoughts fill their crystalline matrices; what ponderous urges impel their movements.

Gneiss

The world turns, ages roll. There is only movement in an endless fiery ocean. We are conceived in the eternal deep, in the infernal womb of the earth. There is fluidity and current and heat; we seethe and boil; turn with the lazy motion of the planet; and wait for birth. We are aware only of a cooling. And with that cooling we lose an essential part of our nature, our elasticity, our liquidity, our coalescence. We become distinct and hard, growing apart. But in this change there is no regret for our loss of warmth and completeness, as within us begins a strange incarnation, giving us identity. Crystals grow: dark and greasy feldspars; blue opalescent quartz; hornblende and biotite; pyroxene and olivine. Energy flows through our crystal veins but slowly, so we are only lightly aware of growth. At last the moment of birth comes near. We strive towards the sun.

Cataclysm. Our mother is young and she plays with continents without concern for her embryonic children. The great land, of which we are a part, is crushed and mangled, and powerful forces drive us back into the depths of the earth again. It is not the warmth of mother's womb that we remembered: it is torture and deformation; intense heat and pressure – shattering our structure, mixing and blending, changing our nature – until we are new beings. Out of adversity comes complexity. For now our veins glitter with new treasures: pyroxenite, needles of anthophyllite, peridotite, dunite, anthophyllite-carbonate rock, garnet, orthorhombic pyroxene, spinel, talc, hypersthene, hypersthene-augite, augite-feldspar, epidote. For 1,500 million years, give or take a few hundred million, Earth's processes uplift and erode and fold so that we gather ancient sediments (muds and limestones), new-born lavas; all heated and
compressed and changed. Augmented with our new wealth, we turn towards the surface again.

Strangely enough, 1,100 million years ago the land surface, which was formed by the ancient metamorphosed Lewisian gneiss, would have had much the same configuration as it does today: rough twisted bumps of rock and small hollows. But there would have been one major difference: whereas now the chaotic appearance of the landscape is softened by grasses, heathers and small hardy trees, in those days there was no life worth talking about to cover the harsh rock.

This land, which was to become the North-West Highlands of Scotland, lay north of the equator at the edge of Laurentia, a continent which included Canada, Greenland and Scandinavia. Although life had appeared by then, it was still very primitive in nature and probably only thrived as yet in the seas; so the great continent was a lifeless, desolate desert, in which the only movement came from the swirl of dusty whirlwinds or the stately progress of huge rivers over its mighty expanse. As the earlier period had been marked by tumultuous upheavals and burials (the eras of igneous and metamorphic rock formations), this was a time of gradual erosion, as wind and water gnawed away at more than 15 kilometres of the higher continental interior. The great rivers carried this material, at first as large chunks of rocky debris, sand and clay, to the low-lying gneiss foreland and buried it in a continually changing pattern of alluvial fans and ephemeral lakes. From time to time, volcanic episodes testified to the still youthful nature of the Earth. Later, russet-brown to purple coloured sands and rougher conglomerates accumulated so that the bedrock was completely buried in a thick layer of sand. Already a new process was influencing the geological record: our earliest ancestors, the stromatolites, slimy prokaryotic bacteria, left undistinguished thin, brittle layers, like filo pastry, in the rocks at Stoer and Clachtoll.

Movements in the Earth's crust brought further continents together: Laurentia, Baltica and Siberia moved south to collide with Gondwana and form a vast supercontinent subsequently named Rodinia by geologists and causing a mountain building episode called the Grenville Orogeny. Lying at the centre of these tumultuous events, the ancient gneiss was further troubled and sediments laid down to the east were metamorphosed by pressure into the Moine schists. Now, subterranean pressures were forcing the great continent to break apart again.

To the east, Baltica was cumbrously splitting away and Laurentia, of which Scotland formed the south-east corner, set off to warmer equatorial regions leaving the rest of the continent at the South Pole. For 400 million years heat and cold cracked rocks; rain and wind tore away at the continental mountains; rivers flowed lazily or burst and flooded. All the processes of erosion combined to trans-form and transfer the rocks of the interior to the eastern coastline and its warm shallow sea. Following the geological principles of transformation and recycling, the red desert sands which had hardened into the Torridonian mountains, were in turn eroded and leached of their rust to form dazzling white quartz beaches and deltas on the coast. By this time, the slimy bacteria had evolved sufficiently to leave their mark forever in the hardened quartz sands and muds.

Life

Underneath the sea where it is warm and calm, there is little to disturb the march of millennia. The moon pulls the tides, river currents swirl and, from time to time, upheavals in the seabed send shock waves round the planet. Curious combinations, ignited by Frankenstein bolts of lightning, have been growing and experimenting with different forms of reproduction. Most are obliterated by time but some survive. There is no reason or design in these ventures: it is all just random chance and mutation and, if there is a law in operation at all, it is most likely to be the certainty of failure. For each new successful adaptation, a thousand others wither away; chance disaster takes out the fittest as well as the weakest. But through thousands of millions of years, life has been developing complexity. Succeeding generations build on the success and failure of others. Then, ever and anon, old Earth arches her back and sloughs off these irritating parasites.

The warm, shallow waters now are home to sea-worms, waving arms to catch minuscule prey, retreating into burrows in the sand. The sea is rich in food: life-forms of all manner of type and size proliferate, but, since all the bodies are soft and insubstantial, no trace remains after death, except the worm burrows filled up with white quartz sand like organ pipes.

In fine dark sand and silt the strangest ancestors survive, the trilobites: hard-shelled sea slaters with articulated bodies, an armoured head, and perhaps a sting in the tail. A most successful and definitive life-form, they spread throughout the oceans of the Earth in all manner of varieties and sizes. Yet these too come to an end, and are succeeded by tiny snails in their millions. Each wave upon wave of life is swept away; some leave their imprints on the pages of the book of time; others leave no trace at all. Finally the great book is closed and the pages pressed by the covering seas until all is bound and finished in the story of the rock.

It is strange how the development of Scotland as a country has shadowed its physical formation. Although sometimes at the centre of continents, for much of its history, Scotland, and in particular the north-west corner, has dwelt at the periphery of lands. Similarly, the political boundary between Scotland and England follows a major geological division: England once lay hundreds of miles away to the south on a different continent. The closure of the ocean brought two continents together, creating a Himalayan-size mountain range in the centre of Scotland and the Moine Thrust over the west. It is only chance which has given us England and the English as our nearest neighbours; would the history of Scotland have been different if Scandinavia or Italy had gate-crashed the party instead?

The Waltz of Continents

The great land is dead. The skin of Mother Earth is fragile and imperma-nent, continually circulating down into the depths of the mantle and resurfacing in an endless cycle of death and rebirth. So the great conti-nent passed into the realm of fantasy and parts of it voyaged out on their own explorations. Now the sea is narrowing again, pulling the southern plate northwards to meet the northern continent.

Land meets land-mass with a resounding crash so slow it is inaudi-ble. Only the stars hear. Buckling, folding, melting, subducting, pulveris-ing, bending, grinding, giant forces rip through the land. Enormous mountains are pushed up; slabs of ancient rock are squeezed over younger ones; the edges of continents are sutured together with volcanic needles: syenite plugs boil limestone into marble; seeping tectonic intrusions lace the mountain sides. Even the oldest gneiss, having resurfaced from the eroded sandstone at a leisurely pace, is unceremoni-ously heaved up to perch self-consciously over its younger sisters.

Unaware of this titanic upheaval, life has crept out of the seas onto the land and in a mere matter of 200 million years carpeted the earth with plants and evolved enormous reptiles, ancestors of the dinosaurs. Our land, however, situated as it is, in the arid heart of Pangaea, is hostile to most forms of life. It is a dry, hot highland only capable of supporting tenacious creatures on the edges of the Triassic rivers flowing south-east to the Tethys Sea. If ever lumbering monsters patrolled these lands, only their bones remain as the relict outcrops of Torridonian mountains: the ridge-backed stegosaurus of An Teallach; the protruding ribs of Stac Pollaidh; and the supine diplodocus of Quinag. By now most features of our curious landscape are in place ready for the next major round in the dance of continents.

In the life of Earth, none of her features last for very long. Like a young woman on the approach of middle years, she changes her cosmetics to disguise the signs of age. Perhaps when she has finally become old enough to accept herself as she is, she will cease her restless movement and fickle reconfiguration. So Pangaea, after a mere 100 million years started to dislocate and drift apart. The Outer Hebrides, always uncomfortable in close relationship with the rest of Scotland, began a decisive separation at the Minch. Later, other more adventurous lands initiated a process which has been followed by their children in later years, emigration to the west. The settlers from Lochbroom, who pioneered the voyage to America on the Hector, were unaware that their new lands in Nova Scotia had indeed once been part of the same continent.

The separation of North America, like its political severance millions of year later, was not accomplished peacefully. The whole of Scotland was raised one kilometre and tilted towards the North Sea. Greater uplift, of nearly two kilometres in places, formed the basis of a mountain chain lining the western edge of the Minch. In Mull, Ardnamurchan and Skye, the rift in the seabed resulted in violent tectonic activity. Volcanoes erupted and swiftly cooling lavas formed basalt plateaus and the curious columns of Staffa. Life must have been particularly precarious here with earthquakes, tsunamis, suffocating ash falls, and a blanketing cloud of sulphurous gases blocking the light of the sun. Throughout the planet the Tertiary period was introduced by mass extinctions. Whether wiped out by calamitous planetary events or collision with a meteor, thousands of species disappeared and, after a reign of two hundred and fifteen million years, the dinosaurs bowed out to more lowly creatures: thus began the Cenozoic Era, the Age of Mammals. Slowly, the land settled down and life reasserted itself, but the shifting of continents and processes of orbital perturbation had set the scene for a newcomer on the stage – ice.

The Age of Winters

In the fourth age of the Earth, the land is at peace. Mother Earth sleeps, dreaming deep dreams of her fiery youth but, like a sleeper, often her face is troubled by expressions: a crease here, a frown there and some-times a gentle smile creeps over her lips. Unbeknownst to her, the shifting continents have altered ancient patterns of circulation and made her climate susceptible to tiny dips in her orbit around the sun. While the continents massed at the South Pole or wandered individually in opposite directions, equatorial currents circled the planet, warming the land and, to some extent, controlling the climate. Now two great land masses block the passage of the currents, ushering in an era of winters which last ten thousand years or more: the age of ice.

We rocks have found a troubled rest. Lying exposed to the weather, we feel no touch of the growing cold. Our vast sandstone barrier pacifies the force of the westerlies and the blanketing snow lulls us into gentle dreamlessness. So deep is our unconsciousness that we cannot feel the weight of ice, the dragging of boulders, the scrape of stones, the polish of sand. In our limestone arteries, silent galleries wait for a thousand years for the occasional quick melt and rush of water carrying newly eroded sediments from the surface. When we wake briefly, although never completely awake, we find the frigid glaciers have cut out valleys, dug troughs and deepened sea lochs. Like hibernating creatures in the brief periods before the return of the ice, we bask in a tepid sun and nurture the strange animals which relish our tundra wastes: mammoth, woolly rhinoceros, deer and bison. But soon the snows return and we fall asleep again.

Each time we wake we find more changes. Each Ice Age deepens our valleys. Each glacier dumps rubbly moraines, moulds kames, terraces and eskers and exposes the old bones of the Torridonian mountains. Each ice sheet presses us down. Each time the ice melts the sea erodes high beaches on our shores. Each time the pressure of the ice relieves, we rise slowly up again. As far as we are concerned, it is only a rhythmic rocking to send us to sleep.

In the deepest of the ice winters, the Late Devensian, which lasted for 10,000 years, the ice sheet lay up to 2,000 metres thick, extending from Scandinavia to west of the Hebrides. Some mountain tops, called nunataks, rose like jagged islands in a frozen sea but, otherwise, all of Scotland and most of England lay beneath a featureless plain of ice. Nothing lived here and the pressure of the ice was so great that it swept away most evidence of previous glaciations. At its last retreat, about 14,000 years ago, apart from a couple of episodes when the glaciers returned to high mountains and lobes of ice pushed down into Loch Broom and Little Loch Broom, vegetation, animals and finally humans slowly colonised the warming land. The interglacial period of present times had come. Notwithstanding global warming, the end of this summer is due and perhaps, some day, the glaciers will return.

Aurora Borealis

Liz Butler

It lit the sky and cast a spell.
I stood quite still, my breath had gone,
and felt as though to the end of time,
I would not see such sights as these.

It weaved across the heavens,
upsetting all earth's plan.
It lasted for some moment more
then with disorder was done.

I waited for a little while,
with a need to see it once more.
But silence answered my longing
with vengeful reply it came
hanging onto the night all about me,
slowly turning my flesh to ice.

Before reason returned I felt vanquished,
desolation and loss were mine.

Robert

Liz Butler

They said that he wouldn't reach nineteen and quite dispassionately
They told his Mum he was a Downs child and a long life was not to be.

Of course she wept, but carried on, caring and lovingly
to give him the life he was entitled to and quite determinedly

he repaid this care a hundredfold with a love that knew no end –
his smiles, hugs and laughter would make the hardest person bend.

When we first met, he took my hand and for everyone to see,
brought me into this precious circle with no prior guarantee

and showed me a love I hadn't known before –
a love that was unconditional and one that I viewed with awe.

And when I married his brother, he danced at our feet,
and two babies later, his joy was complete.

They said that he wouldn't reach nineteen and his family lived in fear
but doctors can be wrong you know – he'll be sixty next year.

Haiku

Charlie Byron

Black Forest gateau
Ebony goo oozed, moist lips
Sticky fingers licked

Silver salvered char
Birch shaded, elongated
Sun glistened ripples

Dice loaded hope tossed
One in thirty-six chances
Dots stare – snake eyes

Vanishing Points
A Linear Perspective Lesson

Charlie Byron

Station eye perpendicular
To vision cone, horizon centre
Planes not parallel
To right angle of sight converge
All day the squadrons pass
In parallels, is this the second front?
Eyes raise, lips part in prayer
To specks that drone across a sky
To points upon a map
Converge to win a war, a peace
I¹m grateful for
If asked what did you do that day?
I saw Armadas fill the sky
With ominous moan
While plotting lines oblique
That vanished off the page
Out of reach.

Walking Back in Time with Heckie

Lily Byron

Old man, you took me up through the wet October fields
Barbed wire fence and fading grass against the blue blue sky
To show me your grave
"What a view!" I said. "Pity you'll be dead!"
You laughed. "Due east and west it is.
There'll be a crate of whisky on the day."
We had to go on up – it was that kind of day
You pointed out the old cart track that led to Lairg
And the path to Gow's wood – a name I'd never heard.
We crossed the fence. "I thought it was 'bad wire'
When I was wee," you said
"You see yon dykes?
We used to catch rabbits there when we were boys."
You showed me where the mushrooms grew – fat and fleshy
Damp-smelling, woody, oven-browned meringue on top
Over more 'bad wire' to the field of burial mounds
Hut circles too. Boy, they knew the place to live!
We had to stand on every hump and wonder
What Altas saw and heard in Bronze Age times
Looking west to the green valley of the Oykel
The clouds casting long shadows
Over Cul Mor, Cul Beag, Ben Mor Assynt
And the gentler slopes nearby
What a view! Down the Kyle to Linside and to Bonar
The sky, Italian Landscape blue, with puffs of cloud
Abandoned crofts all round. "Let's go and look at that one
Where old Hughie was brought up – Clashbuie was its name."
But only he remembers, being ninety years and more.
You, now a boy, agree to cross another ditch, another fence, to see.
A stout wee house it must have been, with thick stone walls
The garden with its trees – ash, rowan, pine, within the dyke
We think we hear the children at their play, the women at their work
The squirt of milk in pail, the rattle of a churn
You sit and light your pipe to think a while
While I walk on, imagining their lives
The work put in, perhaps two hundred years ago

Clearing stones, building walls and houses
Planting trees and crops to make a living
And now, no crops, no cows, no people – only sheep
We must turn back for home, but on the way you point out the barn
Where horses pulled the threshing mill
And Uncle's fields, where you lads earned some cash
At tattie-planting or at the hay, when horses took the harvest home
"We walked to school, thirteen of us", you say,
"We loved the master – kind, imaginative with lovely singing voice.
I'm glad I was born here."
At night I take you home in my car
"Reverse as far back as you like", you say.
"As far back as the Stone Age?" I laugh.

Eleanor

Lily Byron

Little one
With big round eyes
You stare at me
And click your tongue
Then stick it out
In search of food
Now your mouth
Is a prim little O
So shocked at
What you see
Now a smile
At secret thoughts
Or is it wind?
A fleeting frown appears
A sigh, another smile
So pleased with yourself
Warm and content,
You smell of milk
And baby clothes
I rock you in my arms
And sing to you
Songs of long ago
You beautiful and
Fragile little treasure
My granddaughter.

The Television

Lily Byron

My father was known as Kenny the Tailor. This is one of his tales.

The wife was long since dead. The bairns were all grown up and away from home. I was on my own. To pass the time, masel' and Towser (the dog) would go down to the Lady Ross for a nip and a pint. Sometimes I would have a go at the "Brighter Billiards" and though I say it masel' I could beat most of them at it.

I was in there one day and I got talkin' to a travelling salesman. He seemed to be enjoyin' my company and he bought me a dram.

"Have you got a television?" says he.

"No, I have not."

"Would you like to have one?" he says.

"Well ... I've been thinkin' about it," I says, "In case I get oot o' touch wi' the rest o' the world. Why are ye askin', anyway?"

"Well", he says. "I'm yer man. I'm a rep for one o' the biggest TV firms in the country. I can offer you a wide selection o' sets."

"Och, I don't know if I could be bothered watchin' it," I says.

"Sir", he says, "without a television in this day and age, you are left behind. Everyone should have one!"

"How much are they?" I asked.

"Oh well," says he, "you can either rent or buy."

"I think I would rather buy if I was gettin' one at all," says I.

"Well, the cheapest would be about £50, with prices goin' up to about £300." (Of course this was a long time ago.)

"It depends on the size of screen you want."

"Oh", says I, "my eyesight is not gettin' any better, the older I get. I would need the biggest screen you have."

Well. he was fairly gettin' warmed up! "We'll need to discuss the price you're prepared to pay," says he.

"Oh", says I, "money's no object!"

He smiled. "Will you have another drink, Mr ... er?"

"Mackenzie," I said. "Kenny."

"May I call you Kenny?"

"What else?" says I.

"Two whiskies, please," he shouts to Morris, the barman.

Well, the more drams we had, the more enthusiastic we got about the TVs. He was all set to sell me the biggest, dearest TV he had.

After he bought me another nip, says he to me, " I'll have to go out to my car and get my briefcase with all the necessary papers."

Whenever he went out the door, I winked at Morris behind the bar. "We're doing alright, eh?"

"Aye, ye are that, Kenny," he says.

Back in came the mannie with his briefcase. Out wi' all the forms. "Now, we'll just get these filled in. Name and address?"

I told him.

"Telephone number?"

"I'm no' on the phone yet," I told him.

"Married, single, or divorced?"

"None o' them," I said. "I'm a widower."

"Oh."

"Occupation?"

"Retired."

"Bank account number?"

"I don't use the bank," I said. "I keep all my money under the bed!"

He laughed and I caught Morris's eye. He was laughing too and shaking his head. "Would you like to pay by instalments or cash on delivery?" he asked.

"Oh, on the nail, " I said. "I hate to be in debt."

"OK," says he. "Just sign here and your TV will be delivered to you within the week. COD."

"That's just grand," says I. "There's just one question I'd like to ask before I sign."

"What's that?" he asked. "Will it run on paraffin? Because ye see, I havna got the power in yet!"

Christ

Kevin Crowe

Christ is black and Christ is white;
Christ is lad and Christ is lass;
Christ is gay and Christ is straight;
Christ is present in the Mass.

Christ is there when we make love,
In each touch and breath and kiss;
Lies beside us as we lay
In the afterglow of bliss.

When we walk the hills and glens,
He is in the gorse and broom;
When we kiss beside a burn,
Christ assures us of a room.

Christ is with us in disease,
Aids and cancer and MS –
Shares the pain within us all;
But we suffer nonetheless.

Christ is with those scarred and scared
By oppression in this world,
With the beaten and abused,
With the tortured and the killed.

Christ is black and Christ is white;
Christ is lad and Christ is lass;
Christ is gay and Christ is straight;
Christ is present in the Mass.

The Young Departing

Kevin Crowe

Golden gorse and purple heather,
The kilts and the pipes and the drams,
The lochs, the burns, the straths, the kyles,
The rugged coastline, silver sands,
The castles, ceilidhs, golf and tartan
Cannot hide the young departing.

Cannot hide the slums of Glasgow,
Nor the oil that flows to London,
Nor the jobs flown with the swallow,
Nor the poor left midst the mountain.
The castles, ceilidhs, golf and tartan
Cannot hide the young departing.

The steel, the mines, the crofts and farms,
Haddock, cod and silver darlings,
The salmon spawning in the burns
All have left or else are leaving.
The castles, ceilidhs, golf and tartan
Cannot hide the young departing.

The fight for freedom means the same
In English, Scots and Gaelic;
From Aberdeen to Stornoway,
From Gretna Green to Lerwick.
The castles, ceilidhs, golf and tartan
Cannot hide the young departing.

Northern Lights, near Durness

Kevin Crowe

Fingers rising
From behind peaks
Growing
Spreading into hands
Arching across sky
Meeting and clasping
Lighting the dark winter night.

A disturbed buzzard spirals from the heather.

He's Upstairs

Wendy Davies

Part One

'Oh, hello! You'd better come in.'

'Ginger, off that chair! Hang on a minute, dear, I'll just brush it off for you. There, that's better.'

'You've come about Frank, haven't you?'

'I saw that nice Dr Patel the other day, and he said that he was going to have a word with you.'

'We have to see him every now and then, about Frank's cough. Anyway, this time, he wasn't too worried. Said there was a lot of it going around. Probably a virus, he said.'

'Well now, you can tell Dr Patel, that we're alright, Frank and me.'

'He's upstairs. He likes to sit up there in the front window, looking down on the road, watching the cars, and the people, going by.'

'Well now, how's everything at the surgery? I hear old Dr Brown's retiring. Well, it's about time. He delivered Frank you know, we all used to have them at home in those days. And what a time we had.'

'He drops in to see us every now and then, just to have a chat. The young ones don't do that anymore, do they? Expect us to go to them every time.'

'Well it used to be so easy. We just used to walk in. It was Dr. Brown's own house, you know. And then we'd sit there in the front room, all warm, with the gas fire going, and that great big table, and nice magazines, you know, the thick, shiny ones. Then he used to call us in himself.'

' Now it's very different, isn't it? All those receptionists, and appointments, and 'Is it urgent?' And that Audrey, manager or something, is she? Well, I remember when she had the florist shop, in the high street.'

'Still, that Sue, in reception, she's good. She'll always fit us in, you know, if I'm worried about Frank.'

'And sometimes I feel that tired. It's such a struggle. Getting him washed, and dressed, and feeding him.'

'Still, we manage.'

'Evie next door, she's good too. She'll always come in and sit with Frank, while I pop to the corner shop, for a few odds and ends.'

'Of course, I miss Dot, over the road. We used to have a good old chinwag, Dot and me. Well, she'd lived in the road as long as I had. But the roads changed so much. As the old ones go, so they make these houses into flats, students we get. Oh, they're nice enough when you bump into them, smile and that. But they go round with these earphones on. In another world most of the time, and the hours they keep.'

'Yes, I miss Dot. I could talk to her, you know, about things.'

'Sometimes in the evenings, I sit here, when I've got Frank nice and settled in bed. I sit down here, and think, about the old times in the road. People were friendlier then. We used to drop in on one another, and look out for one another. Well it's very different now isn't it? Now everyone's so busy.'

'Anyway, sometimes I sit and think, and wonder, you know; what if ..?

'What if Frank hadn't have been born the way he was, and if he hadn't have upped and left us like that, then, I wonder, how it might have been.'

'Still doesn't do to dwell, does it? We get by, plenty worse off than us. Well, you must see it in your job, dear. I bet you see some cases, don't you?'

'Sundays are bad. They drag by. Frank gets restless on Sundays. Well, the road's so quiet. I don't know where everyone gets to. They all get into their cars, at about 11 o'clock, and then they don't get back till evening. Frank doesn't like the television, you see. He can't follow it, and he gets very restless.'

'Still, then Monday comes round, and it's all busy again, and we're alright again.'

'So you can tell Dr Patel that we're alright, Frank and me. And no, we don't need any social workers, or carers groups.'

'Of course, if you wanted to pop round again, just for a chat; well, you'd be very welcome.'

Part Two

'Hello dear, I thought it was today you said you were coming.'

'Well, how are you? You said you were having a little holiday. Did you have a nice time?'

'Well, we had a bit of excitement here. Right out of the blue, our Joan turns up with her Ted. Well, she said that she'd sent a card, but I don't remember getting a card. Well, I know I didn't, because I always put them up on the shelf, in the kitchen. They look nice all together there, and it brightens the place up a bit.'

'Anyway, in they come. Luckily I'd had a bit of a tidy round the day before. She's all over us, brings in flowers, and a big tin of biscuits. Says we can all go out for something to eat. Well, I felt a bit awkward about that, you know, having to dress up. And I never know how Frank's going to be, and he doesn't like change. So I said if they stayed in with Frank, I'd nip out and get a few pork chops, pop them in the oven, and they could be cooking while we were talking.'

'Very chatty she was. He sat there a bit awkward like, but then he always was a bit like that. Anyway, turns out, their Tracy's done very well for herself. Did hairdressing at the college. Well that was no surprise, the hours she spent doing her own hair. No one else could get into the bathroom, and the colours! Well now she's working in one of those big London salons, ever such good money. Different matter with their Jason though, he had to come out of the army. Something must have happened. They didn't make much of it, but you could tell they're disappointed.'

'Of course she doesn't fool me, with all her chat, and flowers and all.'

'You see she's after this house. She's hinted. Say's it's big enough for all of us. And how do I manage, rattling around here, just me and Frank?'

'Well she's not getting it. This house is mine, by rights. I've earnt it. It was me who looked after mum and dad for all those years.'

'You see, when I found out that I was expecting. We, that is Frank's father and me, well we moved in with his parents. A bit awkward it was to start with, but eventually they came round. Well, she did anyway. Even started doing some knitting, like she was looking forward to it. And I used to help her with the cooking, and the washing, and the time went by, and then, Frank was born.'

'Like I said, Dr Brown delivered him at home. There was a nurse who helped him. Starchy cow she was. Nurse Marchant.'

'I had a terrible time. I can still hear myself screaming. And there was Dr Brown with his sleeves rolled up, sweating he was, and her, fussing over him, never mind about me!'

'Only seventeen I was. Anyway, at last, Frank was born, and oh, the relief. But somehow I couldn't stop sobbing, until she gave him to me.'

'All wrapped up he was, but I could feel him, warm and soft under the cover. And his little face. It was the dearest little face I ever saw. And

I was just going to undo the cover to look, when she, that witch, took him from me. Out of my arms!'

'And then everything went black. And it stayed black. Like being in a black tunnel, and I couldn't find a way out.'

'I remember her, coming in to see me, telling me to pull myself together.'

'I took one of the drawers out of the chest, and I made it into a little cot. So I could have him close to me, next to the bed. So I could look at him.'

'Dr Brown used to come and see us. Then one day he brought someone with him, another doctor. Smarter than Dr Brown he was, you know, had a proper suit on, not like that old tweed jacket Dr Brown always wore. I could hear them talking. Then I heard the word hospital. Well, that shook me up. I mean, who would look after Frank if I had to go into hospital?'

'Somehow I managed to get myself up. I just had to. For Frank's sake.'

'I managed to get into a little routine.'

'Time went by.'

'Then one day, he, Frank's father that is, well, he didn't come back from work. We started getting worried, and I went into the bedroom, to look through his things. Then I found this note. Shaking I was. I knew it must be something bad, for him to write a letter. Said he'd got a job up North. Said he'd let us know.'

'Well, you can imagine how they were to me then.'

'I just bundled our things together, and we came back home.'

'They weren't too bad really. Mum was good. I think she realised what I'd been through.'

'So we stayed.'

'And of course I looked after them both as they got on, until ...'

'Well, I feel quite worn out, going all through that. And I've probably kept you too long.'

Part Three

'Hello dear. Oh, I have been looking forward to you coming round! I've felt so ...'

'I hardly know where to start. So much has happened. Well, firstly I'm moving. No, I'd better tell you the story first.'

'You see, we had some visitors. Oh, it was such a lovely surprise! A week last Sunday, just as we were feeling a bit at a loss, you know, that lonely Sunday feeling.'

'The doorbell went, and it gave me a bit of a start, well I wasn't expecting anyone. I didn't recognise her to start with, then she smiled, and I could see the likeness at once. Dot's grand-daughter! You remember, my friend Dot across the road. Ever so close we were. I missed her something terrible when she died. Flu it was. That last bad winter.'

'Anyway there they were standing there. Mary, all grown up, with her young man, and they'd got a baby, a dear little girl. Sarah they've called her.'

'They'd decided to visit the road again. A sort of a trip down memory lane. You see, when Mary was young, Dot often used to look after her. While her mother worked. I used to take ... Well, with me often being across at Dot's, I got to know her really well. Lovely little thing she was. Used to like dressing up. I can see her now, tottering about in Dot's shoes, with one of her dresses on, and one of those feather boa things round her neck. Oh, Dot had some lovely bits and pieces. And how we laughed! Nice times they were.'

'You can imagine how pleased I was to see her again. After all this time! I got them in and made a pot of tea. And luckily I'd still got that nice tin of biscuits, you know, the one Joan brought me.'

'So, we were all sat down, and Mary was chatting away. Turns out, she's lost her mother recently. Cancer of course! Only 56 she was! And what with the new baby! Well, she was missing her. I mean, you always want your Mum then, don't you? So they thought they'd look us up.'

'Oh, it was so lovely! Having someone call! You know, who really wanted to see us. And on a Sunday too!'

'Like I said, we were all sat down, and suddenly, Mary gets up, and walks across, with the baby, and puts her into my arms!'

'Little angel she is. All warm and soft, and smelling of Johnson's. And, oh, I felt that choked up! I couldn't say a word. Just looked down at her dear little face. And of course, it took me right back, to when Frank was born.'

'And something happened, inside my head. And it came to me, as I looked down at her, all chubby and pink, and so full of life! That dear little Frank, who I held in my arms, all those years ago, is dead!'

'You see dear, I'm not really mad. I know Frank isn't upstairs. It's just that when they told me that he'd died, after he was born, my head was so foggy, I just couldn't take it in. And later, in that black tunnel, the only thought I had in my head, was the feel of him in my arms, and the picture of his dear little face. And I couldn't let it go.'

'And I suppose, when I managed to get up, and seemed a bit better, I got into this little routine of looking after him. And well, people went along with it. I suppose they thought, well ...'

'You can imagine the state I was in, after they'd gone. I sat down here for most of the night, with Frank's shawl around me. Yes it's real! Didn't even care about the electric! And the next morning, I just knew that I'd got to get it all cleared up, and out into the open.'

'I telephoned the surgery, and luckily it was Sue who answered. And she could tell the state I was in. Got me fitted in with Dr Patel. Well he was so nice. Let me cry it all out. And then, I didn't have the strength to walk home. So they called me a taxi, and that Audrey made me a cup of tea, while I was waiting, and then when I did get in, I just fell asleep right here in this chair.'

'So, I've been doing a lot of thinking, and I want to start afresh. I've decided to move. I've got my eye on one of those bungalows, you know, the one's that back onto the park. Lovely they are! I remember when they were being built, central heating, and all on the flat. I told Dr. Patel, and he's going to write to the housing people for me.'

'So our Joan, and her Ted, can have this house! They're welcome to it! It gives me the creeps now! I've stayed down here, sleeping in this chair.'

'But there's something else that's keeping me going. Something really special to look forward to! You see, young Mary, and her Brian, and little Sarah, well they visited me again. And they said did I mind if they dropped in on me every now and again, on a Sunday she said. Well, Sundays are so flat, when you haven't got a family, aren't they?'

No Way Out

George Doull

I slowly awoke squeezed tightly into the cramped confined posture of an unborn baby whose mother had long since died from alcohol poisoning.

With effort my sleep-encrusted eyes blinked open to be greeted with nothing but thick impenetrable blackness. My body was dehydrated hollow and weak as if I had been injected with a giant hypodermic needle and had been sucked completely dry. When I tried to move a growling mad pain pulsing with every heartbeat through my body brought me round and jolted me into an agonizing claustrophobic state of gloomy consciousness. My whole past became a dull blur as I fought to recall where I was or what I had done. Any recollections dissolved as I choked and gagged up a huge stream of hot sticky vomit all over myself .Groaning I tried to sit up but instantly deflated as my skull connected hard into something solid just above my head. Terror shot through me. I was boxed in. With panic rising I rubbed my throbbing skull and frantically pushed the lid of my tomb to find it opened quite easily.

I must have looked worse than Frankenstein's monster on a bad trip as I emerged from some kind of stinking container and wobbled out into a boiling humid suffocating reality I found it impossible to understand. I found myself gasping for air as dense thick black smoke engulfed and smothered me. Thin chinks of sunlight filtered in through gaps in the darkness. Not far away a fire was raging furiously. My mind quickly buzzed with a static of fear. I knew I had to get out of there fast or I was doomed. My lungs were bursting. Blood pumping through my head rang in my ears like hammer blows to my skull. In a frenzy of panic-stricken terror I plunged blindly forward in a desperate attempt to escape the deadly belching fumes. I stumbled and pitched onto my hands and knees but kept going clawing and grasping at anything on the ground that would pull me closer to safety. Every movement sent increasing bursts of white-hot agony through my body. I knew I wasn't going to make it. With one last tremendous effort I threw myself headlong into the billowing blackness before I passed out.

It could have been seconds before I came round. It could have been hours. When I recovered I found myself lying face down in what I first imagined to be a gigantic rubbish tip. The awful realization became frightely clear the moment my head stopped spinning and my senses accustomed to the decaying atmosphere I had stumbled into. Memories slowly started seeping back into my shattered mind as I stood stunned with disbelief and tried to make sense of it all.

It was like a vision of hell. The plane had come down with such monumental impact it had created a massive crater for itself in which I was now standing. The choking heat and the stench of burning was unbearable. Debris had been scattered everywhere. Bodies littered the ground as far as the eye could see. Several were burned beyond recognition. I had to get out of there in order to be able to think straight. Wide accusing sightless eyes drilled into me and dead hands tugged at my legs as I jostled my way through the decomposing mass of death. I could vaguely remember swigging from a large bottle of complimentary beverage before having to go and relieve myself. Next thing I know I am waking up in a state of hallucination and sheer terror. A toilet cubicle had saved my life. It was a miracle I had survived. It was plainly obvious there were no others.

Oh God, no. That small girl, the one with the beautiful blond curly hair and blue eyes who kept making faces at me from over the back of her seat during the flight. It was her. I was sure of it. Only now her bright warm cheeky smile was frozen in a silent hideous silent scream and her hair was a tangled mess caked with blood. Both her eyes were missing. I turned away from her and retched. By the time I managed to crawl out of there I had thrown up several times and was sobbing uncontrollably. As I crawled over the edge I collapsed half expecting a rescue team to haul me off to hospital. What lay beyond was an endless sea of sand that stretched as far as the horizon. There was no sign of life. The sun was bigger and more monstrous than I ever thought it could be. The heat that beat down on me was as smothering as the smoke had been. And from the enduring pain I was aching with thirst. A thirst I soon began to realize I would never be able to quench.

I shot up in bed with the scream in my throat. Emma was lying next to me fast asleep.

Thank God, oh thank God, it was only a dream. I fell back onto the pillow and exhaled an explosive sigh of relief. I was drenched with sweat. The nightmare was still vivid. I did not sleep again that night.

Six months later Emma and I split up after four years together. She moved back with her parents while I kept the flat and got on with my life. I started dating other girls and never saw or heard from her again. I soon forgot about her.

When I did meet up with her again almost a year later I got the shock of my life. I was walking down Oxford Street when I saw her. She was sitting in a shop doorway on the corner of Regent Street and Oxford Circus. A manky-looking sleeping bag was rolled up next to her. She was dressed in rags. She looked terrible.

I stood there for a long time before crossing the busy street and walking up to her. 'Any spare change,' she asked weakly holding out a plastic soup cup half full of small change as I approached. She did not seem to recognize me. I kneeled next to her. She eyed me warily. 'Emma', I said softly, 'it's me, Paul'. After a long tense moment her eyes lit up in recognition and shone with tears. 'Paul, oh God, Paul,' she gasped. Her voice sounded hoarse. Her face was smudged with dirt. She looked as if she hadn't eaten for a while. Christ, what had happened to her? This was not the flamboyant temperamental Emma I once knew. There was so much I had to know. I still cared for her.

I took her to a cafe and began asking questions. She was very subdued and dismissive. I talked her into coming back to the flat and she sat quietly on the sofa while I made two steaming hot mugs of coffee. I sat facing her. Her head stayed down and she was quiet for a while. I did not press her. Eventually she raised her head and began to speak. 'Not long after we split up I met this guy,' she told me. 'Jerry, city bloke, flash, treated me well. He seemed like a swell geezer, he was charming. I didn't know he was into things, drugs, black magic, orgies. That kind of thing. One night he took me out. I don't remember where. He spiked my drink, drugged me.'

Tears ran down her face.

'He raped me, Paul. There were people there dressed in black. They had a small kitten. I had to watch it being drowned in a basin of water. They laughed and told me I was next, then they all had me. I could see their faces so I knew I was dead. It was horrible. They tied and gagged me, then they drugged me again and I blacked out. Woke up in a skip at the bottom of a derelict builder's yard. There were black bin bags and other rubbish piled on top of me. I escaped and wandered the streets stark naked and half dead until this couple found me and took me to hospital. Those bastards were caught. I was lucky; I think they tried to kill me. Thing is, it screwed me up: I'll never be the same. I quit work, blew it with my family. I've been living on the streets for three months. I don't know what to do.'

I cradled her and we both wept.

She came back but within a week she just vanished. I contacted anyone who might know her whereabouts. I walked the streets. I tried everywhere. She had vanished.

Then I heard the news. Her parents contacted me. The police had fished Emma's body out the Thames. She had drowned herself. I was crushed. I felt responsible. I had let her down. At the funeral I was overcome with grief. I was devastated. The pain stayed with me. I had to get away. I needed a break. I decided to take leave from work and get out of London. I contacted my brother Clive in Melbourne and arranged a month-long holiday in Australia. I began to feel better already. I couldn't wait to leave.

Flying was a new experience for me. The prospect was almost as exciting as the holiday itself. I boarded a jumbo at Heathrow and was directed to a window seat. Perfect. I could sit and watch the world far below. We took off and I was thrust back in my seat as the jet soared high into the sky. A vast sea of cloud obscured the view so I sat back, relaxed and soon drifted off to sleep.

When I woke we were well into the flight. I was offered a complimentary bottle of plonk which I swigged back greedily. Before long my head was spinning.

Suddenly a pretty girl about ten years old appeared over the seat in front and pulled a face at me. Cheeky thing. I pulled one back. She giggled and vanished. A second later she jumped back up and stuck out her tongue. She had beautiful blond curly hair and the clearest blue eyes I had ever seen. She was with her father. I wondered what her mother looked like. I was hit by a strange feeling of deja vu as I watched her. I had seen her before. I was certain of it. Where was it? I tried to think. No, impossible. Maybe she reminded me of someone. My bladder distracted me and I got up to use the men's room. As I did I looked round at the other passengers. Most of them were vaguely familiar. This is bloody scary, I thought, as I made my way to the toilet.

Iambic Pentameter

Maureen Erskine

Do I write in rhythm and rhyme?
I ask myself this all the time
To show I know, what will I write
At the moment all I'm writing is pure tripe.

Now there's a subject I could choose
To write about tripe, what's there to lose?
I'll have to talk to a butcher man
To learn as much as I possibly can

I looked tripe up in the dictionary
Five definitions given and they all vary
I've settled for claptrap which is very true
Of the tripe I'm writing just for you.

I seem to be going round the block
I must stop writing and take stock
Does this poem have rhythm and rhyme
Or has it all been a waste of time?

The Crossing

Ray Forsyth

Do you remember the phosphorescence?
The way it sparkled and jumped
and looked like fairy lights?

And do you remember how the children
leaning over the edge of the boat,
dragged their hands through the water?
How they held their fingers up before their faces,
and how they laughed as the light dripped?

And do you remember how the moon shone on the dark
water
and how the boat slashed the flat sea
into a strange script,
fanning out from the bow's prow?

Aye, it was a rare crossing that night.

The Meeting

Ray Forsyth

Coming across you like that in the street
quite disarmed me,
took me by surprise.
The surprise was glad – unexpected, till
the cannonball hole in my chest told me
otherwise
and I was glad we were going different ways.
The hole lies round and dark and deep
a cavity against my heart.

Loch Roe

Mandy Haggith

dazzling lights on the loch
flottilas of mysteries crowd
into our harbour

a notebook
a tree branch
a blue plastic bottle
three white feathers

I surrender
defenceless against the loch's advances
its seduction

as effortless
as inevitable
as cloud

A Highland Landscape
(after Peter Finch)

Mandy Haggith

1.
To live in the Highlands

is to be grumbled about
by heroes from Norman MacCaig poems
in yellow wellies

is to have a tobacco-stained finger
lifted in dismissal
from each passing place

is to be baffled
by muir-burning crofters
with barbed-wire and wool eyes

is to be reminded
that this century's arrivals
cannot compensate for
nineteenth century clearances.

And the land, the land,
the woolly-maggot-riddled, midge-infested land,
burned and grazed
until its ribs show through,
starved
by shortbread-tin-majestic stags.

To live in the Highlands
is to love bogland
and to be afraid
of factors.

2.
History has been re-lived
a lost heritage
wept for
regained
then tossed away.

A heritage
that sang beauty to the world
through Gaelic words
and Clarsach strings.

A heritage
stolen once before
when township homes were razed
their lazy beds rampaged
their stewards flung
to distant lands.

A heritage
of cows and birches
torched by tacksmen
who handed on their flames
and their English language games
to their downtrod tenants.

A heritage
that is still here
humming on quiet poets' sheets,
hanging onto crags in rocky glens
where teeth and fire can't reach.

Look at the Highland landscape,
look down from the mountain tops,
the deeds must be rewritten properly,
for Highlanders cannot endlessly cut peats
on absent people's treeless property.

Flotsam

Mandy Haggith

When they brought the structures into the loch
they were not meant to stay here long
but no-one knew quite what to do with them -
old bits of fish farm cages, raft, walkway, ring,

and once they'd weathered a few big storms,
rocked and bobbed at the end of their mooring,
people got used to seeing them here
even though they're ugly and don't belong,

like the rest of us, they've somehow blended in
and the year moves monthly on and on,
yet inside the ring the water is always calm,
and anchors corrode but still hold tight to the ground.

Slimegarden

Mandy Henderson

Singing, she rocks to the water. A clear beam of sound, tuneless, every-day. She cradles her home-made soap in one hand. Loch is bitter and soap soft with the new oil. Slipping green underfoot, lathering her body, then sinks to watch the bubbles dissipate into scummy threads of pearl. Happy with her soap Coro curtsies into the water to rinse. But something deep in the limbic brain scares. Blood pumps and eyes dart, looking for the source. Can't find it. She breathes and sucks her world in for the last time. Breathing out and she chokes on alien air. Splashing back to shore, looking back to where she had bathed. A milky stain is still lying on the surface of the water. It develops tentacles that spread out from the centre and lie there rudely, refusing to go. Coro sidles back to the shoreline to crouch down, breathing shallow. To touch the water. To be touched by a crust of horror. This is not her loch. This isn't anybody's anymore. She charges back to the croft, flinging the soap backwards through the fine summer's eve.

Rocky Red woke early, eyes round to a yellowed ceiling. And took a deep breath. A smell sent her hurtling out of bed to look for the source. Was it downstairs? No. All seemed fine; nothing on fire, no odd soaps cooking. Mum seemed fine, although she'd been in strange form the night before and seemed to be mumbling in her sleep right now. Well, it was early. The wee lass hauled on jeans and jumper, knowing full well that the source of the smell had to be outside. She had the distinct feeling that it pressed against her home and could imagine the windows bulging inwards. Out the front door. Down to the beach.

"What is it?"

"Don't know – yet."

"Whatdya mean – yet?"

"Well, I always get to the bottom of stuff. You know that, Fluke."

"What a stink is coming from it. Just like dog shit."

"It's nothing like that. Nothing at all. Anyway, what do you know, bloody baby?"

"You're a know-all, Rocky. I think it smells of shit. And looks like a big old dead whale."

"Nah, can't be. Doesn't look like it's floating, and there's some thing sticking up out of it. It looks like a tree, or something."

"Well, I think it's a blubbery old whale. Dead. Dead as a doornail. Bloody dead, so there."

"Stop your swearing, Fluke, or I'll get some of mum's worst soap and stuff it in your gob so hard you'll taste it till you're sixteen."

"Well, I'll stick some of it so far up yer arse bubbles will come out of your bellybutton."

"You're disgusting, Fluke. They ought to have left you out in the heather when you were born."

"Okay then smart arse, what do you think it is then?"

"It's a slimegarden."

"What?"

"See that thing sticking up – it's a gooey sort of tree, and these other wee drippy bits are flowers. Look, they're purple."

"I can't see any drippy bits."

"You're blind."

"You're making it up. It's a whale and it stinks, just like you, Rocky Red."

Fluke stomped the heather, a ruddy stomping machine. Stone kicking, pouting, spitting. Rocky Red, freckled child of moon and glen, picked a scab and stared. The half light of dawn hid more than it revealed. The thing in the loch did not move, did not float. But it stank blackly and she knew it wasn't a whale.

Slow move. Sable stain. Puce steam rising. Children blether, giggling. Scared.

The sun was just skimming the hills when old man Comfrey saw Rocky Red perched on a petrified tree trunk close to the edge of the loch. He diverted from his usual early morning amble and strode over to her, an old bit of root ginger, frayed in brown tartan.

"It's far too early for a lass to be out with no coat on. Here, put this on, and no nonsense."

"Poo, but it stinks of tobacco, Comfrey. I'm not cold, just a bit shivery. Just looking at the slimegarden."

"What the devil …"

"Look, there's a tree growing on it. And I'm even seeing some colours now; purples mainly, but some pink and dark blue."

"What the hell …"

"Fluke thought it was a whale but he doesn't know his arse from his elbow. I'm taking the dinghy out to see it properly."

"You'll do no such thing. Come on now, back home. I'm sure your mum will be up by now. I don't know what is out there but it looks and smells like trouble, so come on."

Old man Comfrey. Furrows deep. Smells warm jelly and sulphur. Gags and spits to the side.

The water of the once loch felt different. Oily. It still lapped the stones and moved the green weed, but it was as though it lived in a different time now. So different from yesterday. The mound in the middle of it did not change. Rocky Red had followed Comfrey for a few minutes before darting off in the opposite direction. In a worried trance he hadn't noticed she wasn't beside him. She sat in her mother's small rowing boat now, the smell of the slimegarden bludgeoned her nostrils with clods of dung and custard. It hollowed her out and refilled her. Her heart, lungs and liver didn't fit her any more.

The old man reached the cottages before he realised that the girl had done a runner.

On the far side of the loch, facing the scattered dwellings, two fishermen stood on a small jetty, regarding the mound.

"Stormmaster, remember yesterday, on the way in, I said I wasn't feeling good. Like my guts were twisted or something. I felt like I was dreaming. The prawns looked at me funny – like they knew something I didn't – and didn't move around that much. I felt plain weird all the way home."

"Aye, well, we all know why that was, don't we, eh Sola?!"

"Nothin' at all to do with that. This was different. A strange feeling. Very strange …"

"Well, not half as damn strange as that monstrosity over there. It's got me. Thought it was a whale at first, you know, first glance. It's certainly the oddest damn thing I've ever seen. Doesn't look like it belongs in this world at all."

"My god, look! There's something moving on it. And it's bloody waving at us!"

"Quick, give me the binoculars. Quickly!"

Sola and Stormmaster took the outboard from the jetty and headed outwards across the loch towards the stinking mound. It was further from them than it was from the village at the other side. They moved slowly through the water, even as the motor gave all it could. The two men looked at each other, saw tension. They both felt the same heave of blood and tissue as the tension wrapped itself cosily around them. And as they approached the thing, both knew that they no longer breathed in the world. Tears were running down their cheeks by the time they berthed at the gland of putrescence rising from the deep.

Upon the island sat a girl, under a tree.

Black sap crawled in channels up its trunk to feed plump leaves. Violet ichor dripped. The men called urgently to her to get into the boat. They bawled. They begged. But they couldn't bear to set foot on that island to get her. Stormmaster looked up into the sky, hearing the sound of helicopters, lots of them. At the same time Sola saw the boats in the distance, military grey. Nasal megaphones shrill. He wished for yesterday.

Coro is standing on the shore, in front of her home. The sluggish water sucks her toes. Hair hangs like ravens' wings. Night-gown brushing knees in satin. Arms reach out to the slimegarden, corded, impotent. Her mouth is open. People are running towards her. Two fishermen sit crying in their boat in the middle of the loch. They look from the smiling, excited girl, a world away from them now, to the woman on the far beach screaming.

The Broch

Harold Lane

MacGraw hit the old misshapen cow on her rump hard with his stick. She attempted to hurry forward, but the narrow entrance constrained the herd, the result being the usual shuffling chaos of moaning cattle and shouting men. When the cattle were housed for the night in the Broch, MacKiltie, the guard dog keeper, began to loosen the dog's chain as MacGraw, cursing all the while, closed the rough-hewn gate with a creaking groan. The guard dog snarled, recognizing the brute within MacGraw's soul, while MacKiltie strained at the dog's chain, holding him back while MacGraw threatened the animal with the butt of his stick. MacCurrock, the gate keeper, closed the inner gate with a clatter of iron and wood on stone. The evening was drawing in while the herd made its way to their byres that encircled the confined interior fortifications. MacGraw raised his voice threateningly as he cursed the gate keeper in his usual way. "You'd let these beasts in, but likely shut the gate against my entry, wouldn't you now MacCurrock?" MacGraw continued as if demanding physical retaliation. "Yes, if you weren't watched carefully you would leave the gates wide open to the enemy, let them march in, steal the cattle some wild night while you slink off with a tribute of their lusty maidens. A fine right bastard you are, never to be trusted, ever, MacCurrock, eh?" The gate keeper glared with fury, holding his fists tight to his breast, spitting on the ground as MacGraw passed. He remembered his father's dire warning when he caught him fighting with his cousin at the age of seven, and knew that for the safety of the tribe he had to restrain his natural wrath. MacCurrock spoke grudgingly to himself. "Better to tame oneself to these insults than to cause disunity, but one day the opportunity will arise to make redress, and I'll kill him, that I certainly will." Conflict had to be kept at a low edge within the tribe as there was enough to contend with now with the 'Lairg Wanderers' warring around this area, eager to steal good grazing land, and to achieve this end, kill all the inhabitants of this eighty-strong community if needs be. Eighty-strong that is, but that doesn't include all the bairns up to the age of seven. Beyond that age all were considered as adults. There was no discrimination, all having to work and bear the grudge of hard living: that's true democracy of a sort, isn't it, when living has reduced to being nasty, stunted and short?

Death came to the people of the shore Broch early. Few lived beyond forty, the prime of life being between seventeen and twenty-three years. After that degeneration set in swiftly, mainly from chest infections and wasting disease, then the men and women were confined to repair and maintenance work. There was no room for mercy. If someone had severe illness that incapacitated them for more than a week or two, he or she would be taken out and put to death, this was the case for the young as well, many of whom never grew into adulthood. The inhabitants of the shore Broch like all the other five hundred over the Highlands and Islands of Scotland existed under extreme duress. Survival was the only thought that kept each and every one going every day from morning till night. Their dreams too were filled with fears, uncertainty regarding the onset of sudden death. The worst disease that seemed to erode the health of these poor people was a strange wasting one, what we would today call cancer. When this became evident, the person would often flee from the Broch and risk survival outside, for he or she knew they would have to face the executioner's sword otherwise. Signs of birth and death were everywhere, reminders of this cruel life of squalor wherein there would be no hope but extinction from it. Lucky were those who were stillborn, or lived for just a few months in childhood.

The elected leader of this band was Rory, the strongest of mind and body, who had attained the age of twenty-five without signs of ill health. Rory was standing brooding dark thoughts scanning over the parapet that encircled the shore Broch's wide circumference. As he looked out to sea, drinking from a large bronze beaker that overflowed with barley beer, he turned, and, beyond the close fields where the cattle had strayed during the day with their armed escorts, towards the trees he discerned movement. Watching intently for a few moments, he called below for a younger man to come up. Roddy, a youngster of seventeen, whose beard was little more than down leaped up and faced Rory. He soon confirmed what Rory had seen. Immediately Rory barked orders of defence and defiance. Gates were checked, missiles placed at the ready, water placed to boil above the entrance gate should the invaders attempt to break it down, and should they attempt access through the first gate the guard dog would be ready to halt their progress. All were given food during the next half hour, chunks of beef together with flagons of the brew. Confidence rose amongst this composite band of humanity as adrenalin defied the earlier desire for rest.

The attackers waited till it was quite dark before approaching, imagining that they would surprise their quarry. They surrounded the Broch on all sides while a contingent came up with a battering ram, then gathered for their assault. Rory roared to his compatriots to attack. Immediately lighted torches were handed to the defenders on the parapet while others threw large stones at the assailants below. There was much excitement and yelling. The storm party attempted to batter down the first gate, while the guard dog barked angrily at this intrusion. At the right moment, Rory ordered the upturning of the iron cauldron by men wearing stout fur-lined gauntlets. The boiling water was poured over their attackers, splashing its way down the sloping stone wall of the Broch. There was yelling and screaming as this defensive measure proved a sufficient deterrent to stave off the assault. A number of men were badly scalded, but only three seriously, this giving time for a second cauldron of boiling water to be prepared. The two parties swore vengeance at each other. The offensive party withdrew bellowing that they would soon be back to destroy everyone in the 'Brora Brigade', calling their fortifications a pile of stones ready to crumble, while howls of "We'll skin you all alive if you try anything," were shouted back in derision and much laughter.

Rory galvanized the eighty-strong clan together into something like a fighting force. His qualities had been tested on many occasions. This test of nerves was little different from one that occurred only eighteen months previously when the 'Lairg Wanderers' attempted an attack one night in a similar way. This attack was hardly a surprise then; on that occasion a number of them had scaled the wall but were swiftly put to death in hand-to-hand fighting. It was well after midnight when the next assault came; this time the battering ram cut from a tall pine required all the attacking force to hold it in position, with some distance along the ram to where the attackers stood, so as not to be caught by boiling water. Though this force were determined they lacked Rory's mental agility.

Rory discerned their approach from the light of his men's flaming torches. He called for the dogs to be ready at the gates. It did not take long for the first gate to be battered down. Immediately Rory ordered the ten war-dogs to be released, and there ensued a skirmish between dogs and men. Rory was not going to risk an assault outside his fortifications enabling the enemy to slip in, close the entrance against the occupiers and create carnage within the Broch. Such a tactic would confuse his men into wondering whether to attack or return to defend their fort. In such moments of fear and indecision they would more easily fall victim to these eager attackers. Rory had experience in the cunning of warfare, his physical strength having caused the slaying of many men both by the sword and by his own hand who had dared to take over his fine stone-clad home bequeathed to this band of rough-hewn pastoralists. Recognizing the risks his people were subject to from the envy and hatred of warring tribes desperate for suitable land to graze their cattle, he always devised plans for any event that would infringe the integrity of his people. With the spirit of foresight and endurance he gathered his archers to send fire-pointed arrows towards the 'Lairg Wanderers'. This was a surprise, a form of defence that Rory with his animal cunning had left till late. The skilful aim of the archers had disabled and killed a number of the attackers furthest from the attacking war-dogs. The desire to continue the assault suddenly developed into a rout. The remaining force retreated with howls and curses into the deep wooded thickness of the night. Rory with a triumphant shout ordered his dogs to finish off the wounded as a reward for their work. The whelps and barks of the dogs mingled with the screams of dying men for the next half hour since the seriously wounded were unable to defend themselves against these trained and ferocious beasts. The retreating party did not care to carry off their wounded comrades as "healing wounds would be more of a hindrance for a sickly, cowardly, and barbarous crew as the 'Lairg Wanderers'". So shouted Rory as, with a defiant movement of his arm, he ordered his beaker to be filled with the brew of victory, and laughed loudly, encouraging his men to rejoice on their night's achievement, while the cries of the dying men outside his Broch made amusement for all who were within it. The guard dog whimpered and howled, tugging at his chain, so eager was he to taste and tug at the flesh that the other dogs were engorging. He was soon let off his chain to join the others in their spoils.

As the light of morning slowly broke over the sea, Rory dozed for just a few moments as he stood against the parapet wall, pissing loudly against it, then strolled around to waken from his heavy-headedness, recognizing that the day ahead might provoke a daylight raid, so the cattle must be well protected by his men and the stronger women who were capable of handling a sword or spear. He was also musing that such a failed attempt to take over the shore Broch would not be likely, though they might create a skirmish when the cattle were out on the pastures. He noted with pleasure that the outbuildings did not appear to be badly damaged. Rory took another long haul of his beaker, finishing off the remainder of his barley beer, when he caught a faint strange humming sound coming from down the estuary. The sound increased and he looked around, and saw two dark shapes floating over the waters, like large dragonflies. He had to rub his eyes, frightened that his senses were deceiving him. He remembered stories of a people two hundred years ago who it was said had a highly developed civilization, lived mainly in peace, and had means for creating power and energy, but that a terrible war laid low their systems and contaminated all the land around. This was just folk tales, there was nothing like this to be seen around today except the remains of what appeared to be their houses. The dragonflies crossed the waters and moved to the grazing lands where they descended slowly. Men came out of them dressed in blue uniforms. By now, many of the other inhabitants had joined Rory on the parapet. Rory turned to them, laughing. "Don't be afraid, my friends, these are not the enemy. I will go out to meet them. Unlock the gates." His comrades were bewildered by what was occurring around them, but trusting implicitly in their leader.

Rory marched jubilantly out towards the men accompanied by Roddy, neither of them wearing swords or carrying spears. He could see that the men in blue uniforms had come with good news from a reborn civilization, one that soon would encompass them and take away the harms that had surrounded them for all these many years.

Questions

Wilma Mackay

1894 – the date, ground into the grey stone,
Will last as long as the strong, rugged house.
My mind wanders with a careless interest
Was Manse life different then –
The beliefs, the passions, the daily surviving?
Or would we today instantly recognise it all?

The pet sheep with the bent leg, hobbling behind the rest
– Another rushing car – nasty speed?
"No," says Margaret, the gentle owner,
"He came into the world like that".
How often do we blame the two-leggeds,
when it is the hand of God?

A recurring thought – Love, if right,
Should be universal.
The Mother Teresa kind. No divisions.
No departments.
The question: who first thought this?
Certainly not me.
Jesus spoke it, Socrates surely knew it.
But who was the first?

Lastly!
Summer day, whisky-amber water
Gurgling over stones and sand in a highland burn
Sun-warmed heather all round.
There are sounds of living, though pleasantly distant.
The day has been before and could last forever.
This my eternity?

To our Visitors – End of Season

Wilma Mackay

The rowans turn red, the day you go away
And autumn comes; you never see this here.
A mini-blast of cold air chills us now and then
Though the sun is still the summer sun.

Spring brought promises of summer's warmth and love:
Now autumn edges into the end of that summer,
The day you go away.

We miss you all, in all our varied ways
But strangely, I cannot explain it here,
With parting comes warm anticipation.

Autumn and winter, as before,
Give time – to reap
The harvest of our summer time together
And store the best memories
To use forever.

The Audition

W. S. MacKay

"You got to enter, man; go for it!" I was being egged on by my buddies in the bar who insisted, "You got to enter man, you are the best!" It was true that I often would win the free drink at the Elvis karaoke competitions when we did the rounds of the local pubs.

The BBC were on a nationwide sweep looking for new talent. Auditions were to be held in all the towns and villages from the Shetlands to the Scilly Isles. And I knew that I was in with a chance. After another couple of voddies to lubricate the vocals, I made my way to the school gym where it was all happening.

In the foyer, there was this dishy-looking blonde giving out forms for us to fill in. Name, phone number, she also wanted to know if we were Pro or Am and what we were going to do, sing, dance, play the fiddle, etc. I had always thought Pro-Am was a golf competition. Was she winding me up?

When I handed back the completed form, Blondie apologised. They were running late, could I come back tomorrow, bringing tapes, props, or backing with me? What a miserable lot the BBC are. You would think that a big firm like that could manage to hire a band to play for the entrants.

Blondie was shuffling her forms as I made my way to the exit. "Hi! Still working?"

She ignored me and thumped the folded forms down on the table. I was about to go, when I remembered the old proverb: they will forgive you if you try, but never forgive you if you don't. So I gave it a go.

"Fancy coming for a drink then, meet the mates and have a bit of a bevvy?"

She looked at me, as if I had just broken wind. Just then a voice called from within the gym: "Anthea, are you ready yet? Get a move on, let's go."

I shrugged my shoulders, "I'll take that as a no then." Stuck-up cow. That night I borrowed the Elvis Karaoke disc from my mate Jumbo in the West End bar, went home, stuck it on and had a rehearsal run of "Are you Lonesome Tonight?" And for my encore I limbered up with "Heartbreak Hotel". Then had a quick run through "It's Now or Never" and "Good Luck Charm". My old man, who was upstairs in bed, hungover as usual, "Shut that damn thing off," he roared, "Or I will come down and throw it out of the window," not appreciating my performance.

What we artists have to suffer!

When I got to the gym next evening, to my surprise there was another half dozen Elvis impersonators before me. Lord knows how many had already been there during the day session. All the others had on the Rhinestone suits with the flares and shoulder pads, and they each had a guitar. I didn't know it was to be a fancy dress do.

There was about twenty hopefuls all waiting in the big room at the back of the platform, some with fiddles, one guy with a piano accordion. Mrs Mackay was there with her daughter all dressed in her ballerina frock, the wee girl was so excited she had to keep going to the toilet. I had taken along my best prop, a half bottle of "Klash-na-koff" vodka. Every now and then I would take a sip. I did offer it around but had no takers.

We all just sat there looking at each other. The only bit of life in the room was the wee ballerina who kept hopping about. I have seen a happier crowd at a funeral. As the vodka started to take effect I said to the guy with the boxie, "Can you play any Elvis? Give us a tune; let's have a ceilidh."

There was a rustle as the Rhinestone suits made to disapprove. But one glower from me and they thought better of it.

I took another swig of voddie. "Give's a bit of Jimmy Shand. Let's get the party going!" One of the fiddlers stood up to go to the loo, and staggered towards the door. He had been sitting by himself drinking black coffee out of a thermos. "Chust wait till I come back," he shouted. The crafty old git, had the thermos filled with OVD; I had a soul mate.

On his return he unboxed his fiddle, and after a few preliminary scrapes and rasps, he give vent to a selection of reels and jigs. I don't know which was which, teuchter heidrom-hoderum stuff isn't my scene, but I did give a hooch here and there, just to liven things up a bit.

Blondie came running through in a tizzy. " Be quiet," she scolded, "the people out front are trying to do their thing, give them a chance. There is no rehearsing in the anteroom. Put that instrument away until it is your turn."

By now the Klash-na-koff had taken over.

"Get stuffed!" I said. "We are going to have a ding-dong. Come on, *come on*, Elvis, give us 'Blue suede shoes'."

The Elvis in the yellow and blue suit stood up. "Why don't you shut up," he said, "and leave the girl alone?"

He was a man mountain six-foot tall and about eighteen stone, but I was not going to take any cheek from him.

"You talking to me?", I asked. "Shut up or put up."

He made to cross the room, so I decided to rush him.

"Stop it, you lout," shouted Blondie. "Get out of here."

She tried to grab me as Elvis swung a punch, I side-stepped and tripped over the fiddle box. The punch landed on the side of Blondie's head and she screamed and passed out. My mate on the fiddle kicked Elvis right in the crotch and as he doubled up I cracked him on the head with a chair. The wee ballerina screamed and peed her pants.

The man out front had already phoned 999. When the police arrived to suss out the scene, the fiddler told them that the big Elvis bugger had gone berserk and hit the lassie. The bobbies slapped the cuffs on him, then Blondie came to. She said it was all my fault, so they cuffed me as well, then took us both to the local nick. I knew my way around there quite well anyway.

Next day up in front of the sheriff we were both fined £20 and bound over to keep the peace. That was me skint again.

Outside the court room, the men from Auntie sprung a surprise. They'd a fly-on-the-wall camera planted in the anteroom. It was the best bit of TV footage that they shot during all of the tour, and they offered each of us one hundred pounds to be allowed to play the tape on air.

"Pay our fines as well, and it is a deal," I said.

The men from Auntie agreed, so we all parted best of pals except for Blondie that is, who I never saw again.

As I headed for the bar to get a wee celebration drink a battered old Ford van slowed down beside me. Still in his yellow and blue suit, Elvis sounded a loud blast on his horn, and gave me the one-fingered salute.

"Who was that?" my mate asked.

"Dunno," I said, "but *ELVIS HAS LEFT THE BUILDING*".

Shin Falls (The Salmon Pool)

W. S. MacKay

The foaming cascading tumult falls,
Into the boiling pool below,
Where on their homeward journey stalled,
The silver fish dart to and fro.

From Greenland's misty icebound coast,
To Scotland's murky peaty streams,
Across the wild Atlantic comes.
This king of fish and anglers' dreams.

The Dead Author

Bill MacKenzie

They've forgotten me again. Every blessed day when it's not raining they shove my chair out here and then forget about me.

"There, William, you enjoy the view." That's the usual chat up line when they are pushing me out. View? There are only a few yards of grass and then a big conifer hedge. 'View' hardly describes it.

Sure it's warm enough just now but just wait until the sun goes round the corner – it gets really chilly. There is one good thing about it, they don't bring those senile soldiers, the Dementia Dragoons, out here. They would be all over the county before you could wink, much easier to keep them in the one room and watch the door. All the company I get is the birds. Sparrows and blackbirds usually, but occasionally I get a rook or a wood-pigeon parading over the grass. They take no notice of me, seems like they know that I'm not a threat.

Lot the staff care. William can't complain, so they treat me any way they like.

William! That's another thing. I've never been called William in my life before. But here it's William, William, William – sometimes from little chits of girls who are young enough to be my grandchildren. When I was their age I called my elders Mister or I'd get a skite round the ear.

I'm getting grouchy, I must watch that. Bad enough being a helpless mute without being a bad-tempered one. And they can make my life uncomfortable if I start being bad tempered. I'll just stay calm. Sweet William, bless him. That's it.

That girl Sally, she's my favourite but there's no disguising that she isn't very bright. I went through a right pantomime to get her to bring some books from the library. I can make an effort at reading but it's such a performance to turn the pages. With this stupid hand it takes longer to turn the page than to read it. But time is something I have plenty of.

"Here love," she smiles, and puts a couple of books on my bedside table. I had a look at them when they got me into my chair and I couldn't believe my eyes. They were romances. Do I look like someone who would read romances? Still, it's no good getting in a paddy about it. I'll try again and see what she comes up with. There must be something decent in the library. If I keep her going she is bound to stumble on something decent sooner or later. It's just a case of living long enough.

We had a couple of romance writers in the group. Pleasant enough old biddies but they did turn out the most awful drivel. To look at them you would never suspect that they had a romantic bone in their bodies. Mind, they weren't the only ones whose appearance was deceptive. That old guy, George, with his la-di-da and his fancy cravat and he wrote the most bloodthirsty war stories I had ever had the misfortune to hear. They weren't much good, too many gung-ho characters all killing and being killed so that by the time he got to the end you didn't know who was still alive and didn't much care. I often thought that a good-sized bomb in the first sentence would have got us to the end a lot less boringly and damn sight quicker.

There, I'm being a grouch again. They were a decent enough group. Not much good as writers but decent caring human beings, though George was the only one to come to see me after the stroke and when he found that I couldn't speak he never came again. He read me one of his stories 'as a treat' and when I wasn't able to make appreciative noises when all his characters had been brutally killed he was a bit miffed. Not that I'm complaining about that, George, stories are a treat I will gladly do without.

I thought Sammy would have come to see me. He was a poet, or so he said, his stuff always reminded me of McGonagall, but, of course I would never have dreamt of saying so. But he did seem a friendly sort of cove. Always worrying about someone who missed a meeting because they were unwell. His concern didn't seem to extend to me though.

You're being a real smart arse, Billy-boy!

Tearing strips off all them folks' efforts. You weren't, perhaps, so bloody brilliant yourself. All that lovely prose, all those beautiful plots, they never seen the light of day beyond that covey of sycophants. How many publishers did you harass? How much did you spend on useless postage? How many trees were sacrificed to provide paper? Perhaps, when they all smiled and said it was brilliant, they were thinking the same about yours as you thought about theirs and that was 'What a load of crap!' The war story man wouldn't like my stuff. The romantics wouldn't cross the road to hear it if I hadn't trapped them by listening to their rubbish.

But there is a difference. I know my stuff was good. I know it was publishable. I know, I know, I know!

I should have been there in Waterstones or Borders signing my latest novel and wondering when I would get to the end of the eager queue. When, with hand numb from signing, I did get to the end of the

queue I'd pop round to Lauders for a pint and immediately be surrounded by admirers who bore my signed work. They would press pints
on me and hang on my every word. No, maybe not. There is always such
a din in Lauders that you need megaphones to carry on a conversation.

Or maybe I would just be passing by Borders and pop in to see
that they'd got enough copies of my novels on their shelves. Casually
I'd stroll over pretending to look at the other names but, thoughtfully
and anonymously, pause to admire the spines bearing my name. Shivers
of sheer delight tingling up the spine. But there's more! This chap beside
me is obviously waiting for me to move on so he can get to my books.
Shift, Bill, but watch.

Yes, yes! What joy. He's skimming along the titles of my books.
Has he read them all and is looking for the new one? Has someone
recommended me and he is trying to find the title? It's difficult not to
step forward and advise him, but I resist the temptation. Ah, there, you
see, he's gone back and picked out *Doxie*. He's reading the blurb, that's
always a mistake. Should I tell him that the best way is just to open it at
random and read a couple of paragraphs? That'll tell you all you need to
know. If you want to have the story spoiled before you start, then read
the blurb.

It's all right, though. He's taken it and headed off to the counter.

Nice! And that's how it should have been. That is how it would
have been if the publishers had their finger on the pulse of the reading
public. The junk they put into print and then they tell me that my novel
doesn't suit their list! What bloody sauce!

Not, of course, that I let that put me off. I kept plugging away
and sending my stuff to those unappreciative bastards but then this
happened. That's the end of it, I suppose. No chance of doing anything
now. I have two options in life now. If it's cold or it's raining they stick
my chair in front of the telly and put the brake on. If it's sunny or
warmish, like today, they wheel me out on the terrace and forget about
me.

No, not really. They don't forget. It just seems that way. See,
here's Sally coming to retrieve me now. It must be time for the indignity
of tea. Then it'll be a few hours stuck in front of the telly looking at
rubbish and then carted off and rolled into bed.

That'll be the end of another exciting and meaningful day. Days
are getting scarce and the scarcer they get the more they are being
wasted. What a mess.

Sally is wittering on, I'm not listening. It'll make no odds, she
knows I can't make any comments one way or the other so she won't be

looking for an input from me. As far they are concerned I'm dead already.

Now there's a thought!

Publishers are keen on dead authors. So are readers. Perhaps they imagine that having passed out of this world they have a special authority – a better insight. So maybe there's still hope for me. Posthumous is popular. Dead is de rigueur.

White Smoke

Susan MacKenzie

watching, waiting
anticipating, praying
the world awaits

wide eyes following
white smoke spiralling
the votes counted

"It's white, it's really white!"
"I wasn't sure at first,
but you're right!"

throngs smiling
applauding the proclamation
philosophy unchanging

apart from the festive celebration
others had hoped for a transformation
for the church to join the changing world

longed for a metamorphosis
give her blessing to the diverse
embrace all her believers

......

opportunity for change
vanished
in a cloud of smoke

An Geamhradh

Siùsaidh NicChoinnich

Sian nan seachd sian

Reothadh, geal le sneachd
Bleideag sneachd an dèigh tè eile

Bodach-sneachda anns a' gharradh
Fàisg air an cith leaghadh
Eoin bheaga mu thimcheall
'S fear na sheasamh air a laimh

Caisean-reòta crochte
bho nan uinneagan reòta

Bhiodh leannanan 'nan suidhe
gu sàmhach air beulabh an teine
taobh ri taobh
a' faireachdainn blàths an teine

Fras an deigh froise
gach latha, gach seachdain

Ag èisdeachd ri òrain gaoil nan lasraichean
A'bhragadaich fo na guthan,
tè 's fear eile, còmla ri chèile
Dèanainn suirghe tro dorchadas na h-oidhche

Chan fhaicear a' ghrian a' dearrsadh
laithean doilleir gun cheann

An doineann gruamach gun stadt
Taighean fo sgalan mòra
Guth garbh na doininn
Mullaichean taigheann reubadh leis a' ghaoth
Beathannan briste leis an t-uisge

Sian nan seachd sian

The Winter

Susan MacKenzie

Appalling weather

Frozen, white with snow
one snowflake after another

Snowman in the garden
Next to a melting snowdrift
Little birds around him
And one standing on his hand

Icicles hanging
from the frosty windows

Lovers would be sitting quietly
in front of the fire,
side by side
feeling the warmth of the fire

Shower after shower
each day, each week

Listening to the love song of the flames
Crackling under the voices
one and the other, together
Making love through the darkness of the night

the sun will not be seen shining
dark bleak endless days

The bleak relentless storm
Houses under large blasts
Harsh voice of the storm
Roofs of houses mangled with the wind
Lives broken with the water

Appalling weather

The Stranger Who Calls Me 'Mother'

Lynne Mahoney

The people around me wear blue. I don't know who they are and mostly I don't really like them. They frighten me, smiling all the time and speaking with their kindly voices. It's just not natural. I know it's an act because sometimes they turn, you see, they attack me when I am walking. I have to walk to try to get back to where I was. They don't understand, they grab me and pull me away from where I want to go. It frightens me when they try to make me go their way, I always seem to need to go in the opposite direction. They don't listen though. Talking, always talking. The voices are kind but loud. Speaking to me as if I can't hear them properly. I can hear them perfectly well and I hate being treated like a naughty child. So sometimes I lash out at them. I'm scared they are going to hurt me. They have never hurt me yet but I don't trust them. So I sit quietly, just for a while to pacify them. Drinking what they offer me, swallowing a little of what is spooned into my mouth. Conforming until it is time to walk again.

I have no choice but to walk. I have a compulsion to get closer to those distant voices, the ones from the past, the ones that haunt me; those voices draw me, familiar voices drifting through the veil of time. Carefully I study the shadows trying to decipher the intricate weaving of so many lost years. Occasionally the distant voices come to me in loud bursts, sometimes in whispers of obscenities. I repeat them, I can't help it, it just comes out. The ones in blue don't like it. They chastise this naughty child. No one can fathom my confusion and so I am left to scream in silence.

They give me a pill. My clothes are removed. I have no say in this because although generally I struggle, they come in pairs, talking, distracting me and they are so very quick. While I stand in humiliation, I catch a glimpse of a woman, a reflection even. She is thin, perhaps emaciated, her hair is white, her eyes are empty. Grey hollows replace the once plump and rosy cheeks. The oversized clothes which had previously been occupied by fleshy limbs and full bosom are removed. She is cleaned. She spits out her teeth to order. Plastic aprons and latex gloves protect the ones in blue, providing them with a barrier between life and death. There is a stench. I watch the reflection: she has no expression, she shows no emotion as they wrap her in a nappy and a cotton nightdress.

I sleep and when I wake there stands a stranger. The stranger calls me 'mother' I'm not his mother though, I don't even know him. Yet as he chats there is something about him that is familiar. I think he reminds me of someone I once knew, a young man who took me dancing. I love to dance. I believe he was a soldier, a very handsome one, handsome and tall. Yes, he was a soldier, I have a photograph of him beside my bed. He looks smart in his uniform and beside him is a young woman. Plump and pretty with a dance in her eyes. She is holding a bouquet, lily of the valley I would say. I had a suit like hers once. Sometimes the stranger picks up the photo and shows it to me. I don't mind, it's a nice picture, so I smile at him and he seems satisfied but perhaps a little sad.

Bunty

Judy Maker

I first set eyes on Bunty when he was very gently brought out from the depths of John's pocket. He was a poor bedraggled looking leveret about two weeks old. He had been soaked in the rain, his fur was ruffled, he was cold and very probably hungry.

I made a bed for him and put him by the fire. While he was resting and drying out John and I had an emergency discussion as we had not the faintest idea of the feeding habits of the hare family although we had kept rabbits in the past which gave us at least a few possibilities to work on.

We decided that the best thing would be to try him with a little warm milk and then some chopped-up grass. I sterilised an ear dropper and made up a mixture of half evaporated milk and half warm water, then picked up the pathetic little creature and cradled him in my hand and tried to feed him.

At first he struggled against the dropper, then got the flavour of the milk and looking rather puzzled he licked his lips. Perhaps he realised that this was food and he tentatively licked the end of the dropper. I carefully put the dropper in his mouth behind his teeth and gently squeezed the milk through; this time he did not struggle and he took down all the milk; after the first lot of milk I had very little difficulty feeding him. When he seemed full I put him down on the floor and watched him. He sat with his ears pricked up, his eyes bright and not a trace of fear. He then started to wash himself, first washing his paws, then briskly cleaning his face and whiskers and then finishing off with his ears.

I then had my first opportunity to see what a really attractive animal he was. His most striking feature was his eyes: they were beautiful large brown eyes, very bright and clear. He had short fluffy fur, which now it was dry showed it to be curly right down the centre of his back. His hind legs in comparison to his size were enormous, while his forelegs were dainty delicate limbs, and it seemed that they could not possibly be strong enough to hold him. He had large pretty ears with black tips and white strips down the edges.

He started to sniff around the floor in his immediate area, found there was nothing to harm him and ventured a little further. It was then that we noticed his limp. He did not appear to be able to stand any pressure on his right foreleg. I picked him up and examined the limb as best I could. There did not appear be a break but to be on the safe side I rang the local RSPCA Inspector for advice. I put the leveret back in his box which I placed in the cupboard next to the fire where he promptly stretched and went to sleep. I was advised by the RSPCA to soak the foot in cold water three times a day, if there was no improvement in a week it would mean the leg was broken, otherwise it was more likely just a sprain. We did this and his foot did improve slowly. In the meantime we still had the problem of making sure that he lived long enough for him to get better.

I decided that as he was so young he would need his milk every four hours, with extra milk at about two o'clock to help him through the long hours. We built up the fire every night that first week to make sure that he would be warm enough to survive without his mother.

During the first two or three days we took to sitting with him on our lap while we were watching television. He became so used to this that as soon as we picked him up he would run up onto our shoulders and for all the world appear to be watching with us.

When this little animal was on John's shoulder the first thing he did was to lick his (John's) cheek and work up past his nose to his eyebrow which he would immediately begin to chew with apparent relish. After he had completed his examination of the face, he would sit on his hind legs and have a good wash, with the occasional lick of the cheek as a re-minder that he was still on his shoulder. Then having finished his ablutions he would sink down on his stomach, stretch out his hind and forelegs, give a little wriggle and go to sleep.

This little comedy was the first in a series of surprises as we had been assured by various people that it was not known for a hare to survive let alone become tame in captivity. Perhaps most other cases had been half or full grown hares, because our Bunty, as we named him, was worse than our cat for wanting, in fact revelling, in affection and fon-dling.

During this first couple of weeks we kept Bunty in his box either in front of the cupboard or inside it if he seemed sleepy. When his foot was nearly better, we would come downstairs to find that he was missing. The first time this happened I was worried that in some way he had got out of the cupboard. Of course this was nonsense as he was still so small he could sit comfortably in the palm of my hand. We found him crouched behind a pair of shoes and as soon as I put my hand out to pick him up he jumped away. This was the forerunner of several mornings on which I had to catch him as he was still nervous before the first feed of the day after being alone through the night. However, he soon calmed down when he saw a tube of milk in front of his nose. He was becoming a very avid feeder and drank half a glass of milk at every mealtime. I started to try him with one or two blades of grass but he would not be tempted. I assumed from this that he would not yet be eating grass in his natural situation or that he was well satisfied with his milk.

As he had by now outgrown his box John made him a small pen. The sides were plywood and the top was small-gauge wire netting. The base was left open so that he could be put out on the grass in fine weather. He appeared to like this arrangement very much and on being first put in the pen he examined it thoroughly, scratched around a little and then settled down, quite content.

To protect my carpet I put several layers of newspaper down before putting Bunty on it. This also delighted my children Andrew, five years old, and Sandra, three, as now they could watch him instead of asking permission to open the cupboard. I still put him in the cupboard for an hour or two every lunchtime in case he was tired. Rightly or wrongly it seemed to make sense to me to treat him as a human child with regard to ensuring that he wasn't allowed to become too tired or distressed.

It was after we had had him about two weeks that he finally got it into his head that he would try some grass after all. He tried about four blades at one feed and then returned to his milk. After that I gave him grass at every mealtime and he graduated on to sweet nettle and cabbage leaves.

When I fed him I used to sit in an easy chair with a glass of milk on a stool by the side of me. As the stool was quite low, my hand was continually going up and down as I filled the dropper. Bunty began to realise that there was his milk and it was extremely funny to see his little head bobbing up and down, up and down as I brought it up to his mouth.

About a week after he started eating grass he learned to drink from a dish. At first I put out his usual mixture of half evaporated milk and half water and he would drink it in one sitting; then I gradually watered it down a little each time. If I had thought he wouldn't notice I was sadly mistaken: he would go eagerly to his dish, take one sniff and hop away in disgust. He didn't even have to taste it to know it didn't suit him. He wouldn't even have bottled milk put in his dish. My cat had several extra dishes of milk in that week of attempted persuasion.

It had been my intention to get him from milk to water so that I could release him back to the wild as his foot was now better and he was a very strong young hare. Secretly I was probably somewhat selfishly delighted that he wouldn't drink water as it meant that he couldn't possibly be set free while he was still dependent on milk. We gave up trying after no amount of persuasion would get him to drink it.

And so he grew. He became more and more fascinating as the weeks went by. One evening I was sitting in the fireside chair with Bunty on my shoulder and I was eating a piece of apple pie. I had eaten as far as the crust when he began to get curious (unknown to me) and he came down to my lap to see what I was eating. I had not been taking a lot of notice as I was watching television when all of a sudden I realised that he was sitting there as large as life eating my apple pie. Believe me, it was all I could do not to burst out laughing and startle him. It was so amusing, he was sitting there with his beautiful ears pricked up, tail wagging, in front of the plate eating apple pie as if it was the most ordinary thing in the world. As you can imagine, after that we tried all sorts of healthy food for him.

He ate cheese, biscuits, dry bread, nuts, cornflakes, oats and the occasional piece of chocolate.

Bunty was an animal with a very curious nature which on occasions got him into potentially dangerous situations. One such event could have proved fatal. I switched on the television to watch a particular programme when to my annoyance nothing whatever came on. I tried all the stations with no results. I then checked out the fuse and the plug – still nothing. The last thing I checked was the wire. To my surprise Bunty had bitten it through as cleanly as a pair of scissors about a quarter of an inch from the back of the set. Obviously it was much too short for me to repair myself so I had to send for an engineer. His face was a picture of disbelief until I produced Bunty. I should say it was quite a story to tell his work mates at the depot.

As Bunty was growing fast we had to build him another pen as the old one just wasn't big enough to contain him and his food and allow him to stretch out in comfort. John built a run in the garden shed and laid a thick bed of straw. At first Bunty liked it and was quite happy in there. Then we had two nights of very severe storms, heavy rain and gales. Bunty went into an absolute panic on both nights and in his fear caught his hind foot in the front wiring and tore his toe nail. We then brought him straight back into the house. He was trembling with fear and he snuggled up right into my neck and hair and licked me. I bathed his torn foot and put him into his small pen after comforting and fondling him. We never put him into the shed again; instead for exercise we let him run free in the living room for two or three hours morning and evening every day.

John used to have great fun playing with him and sometimes Bunty would get into the spirit of the game and sit on his hind legs like a kangaroo and challenge John to a fight. John invariably lost as Bunty's claws were almost as sharp as a cat's and he could scratch equally as well. This play was a good way for Bunty to learn to fight for when he was returned to the wild. Although we didn't like the idea we knew that eventually this situation would arise.

When he was tired he would come and sit by my feet then jump onto my lap where he would have a good wash, including my hands in the process, stretch out and completely relax. Even when relaxing a hare is always prepared for danger but to my surprise on a number of times he fell fast asleep whilst on my lap. This was when I knew I had won the complete trust and confidence of one of Nature's most private and wary animals.

One day a friend of ours brought his New Zealand white doe to see Bunty and watch his reaction on being faced with a female rabbit. She was a beautiful animal in superb condition, the only thing was she was fully grown and therefore twice the size of Bunty.

At first he was very unsure and crept under the fireside chair and watched her. She was very placid and just sat there on the carpet. A few minutes later Bunty came out and went to her sniffing, with ears erect. She decided to return the curiosity and a moment or two later they were no longer wary of each other and were getting quite friendly. Suddenly Bunty shook his head, flicked his ears and shot round the room like a bullet from a gun. He proceeded to dance around in the middle of the floor, jumping and prancing, twisting in mid-air and zigzagging until we felt quite dizzy just from watching him. What a privilege to see this wonderful event! This must obviously been his courtship dance as the doe responded by stamping her foot on the floor with her hind leg. She went under the chair and raised her tail which to us appeared to be an invitation to mate. Nature would not follow the expected result due to the difference between the two animals' genes and of course their sizes, although it would be most interesting to know the possibility a mating a rabbit with a hare. Anyway, we shall have to see in the future; in the meantime we shall more than likely get a doe for Bunty purely for companionship.

Bunty was now three and a half months old and shortly after we spent a great deal of time by the door. We realised that he was wanting his freedom. He had spent many lovely warm Spring days out on the lawn in his pen but this time I took him out in my arms, saying my goodbyes in tears. He sprang from my arms, sped away through the fence, along the side of the barn and out into the open fields. He moved with almost unbelievable grace and it was a wonderful way to say goodbye.

I like to think that he remembers us and maybe even one day will come to live somewhere near our cottage. This is of course probably wishful thinking, as we had grown to love Bunty more than any other pet we had known. Still, perhaps next Spring there will another leveret which needs loving care. In a way if there is we can re-live the wonderful experiences we had with Bunty with a little more understanding and knowledge.

The Burn

Stephen Marrable

The wind whistles a haunting tune,
As hills look down upon the banks,
While the pines stand guard,
Above this mighty burn.

Eagles soar throughout the sky,
Deer roam and play,
And otters swim,
Within the mighty burn.

With autumn tones fading,
Allowing the winter to creep in,
The first snows falling,
Cooling the mighty burn.

The pines shiver as the cold dark nights draw in,
Summer birds migrated,
As the winter slayer sets with,
Around this mighty burn.

A lonely piper plays his tune,
To the screams of yesteryear,
And the ghosts come a-roaming,
To this mighty burn,

The waters that flow, once red with death,
The screams that do not fade,
So our lonely piper plays his tune,
To remember the fallen dead,

With the beat of the drum,
A clash of the sword,
So our men are slain,
The mighty burn that did see,
Lies down her weary head.

Epiphany

Anne Oien

It must have been there in that winter
Far up in the arctic lands
That a blessing came to a woman in pain
A treasure to hold in her hands

The journey up north was a nightmare
The runway a maelstrom of fear
She clutched at the arm of a stranger
In the wake of the man she held dear

The warmth of the welcome surprised her
Far away from her own kith and kin
It took her straight back to her childhood
And it melted the heart of her man

The home was an old wooden farmhouse
Set apart by the mountains so cold
The small rooms were bright, the stove was alight
The furnishings burnished and glowed

The women had worked since the autumn
Preparing the yuletide fare
There were hot breads and stews and warming home-
brews
And it thawed the cold feet of her man

In the time of the Bible story
The magi brought gifts rich and rare
But the gift she received that winter
Was precious beyond compare

Now here back at home she rejoices
In spite of the wind and the rain
For epiphany brought the joy that she sought
And happiness came from that pain

Memories of a Lairg Childhood

Elizabeth J. M. Ross

One of my earliest memories is of the shops being open all hours. During the week I think it was until 7 p.m. but on a Saturday until 9 or 10 o'clock. I can remember waking up, it being pitch dark, hearing voices and a bell ringing. I started to cry because I was afraid. Then I remember my father coming to light the 'Pixie' lamp and telling me he was still in the shop.

On reflection, I realise we had all the shops we required, from the butcher and the baker, to the blacksmith and the tailor, although I doubt if we appreciated the fact.

It would be possible to count the number of people who owned a car and very few people had a telephone. We walked everywhere or cycled if fortunate enough to own a bike. Families walked to church from Terryside, Saval, Tomich, Torroble and Gruids. Some went twice on Sunday which was a very quiet day. Even those families who didn't go to church did no work except that which was absolutely necessary.

I remember the milk being delivered by horse and cart, by the MacKay family of Rhianbreck. The customer took a jug and received the milk from a tap on the churn at the back of the cart. The horse stood patiently while news was exchanged, but knew the routine so well that it could stop at the various houses by itself.

As a horse was essential to every crofter, Adam Munro the blacksmith was kept very busy shoeing them, putting rims on cart wheels and doing other necessary jobs. With progress, however, Willie Mowatt came from Caithness and his tractor ploughed the fields instead of horses.

Christmas was not celebrated as a major event and all the shops were open on Christmas Day. Some of the older people even considered it a pagan festival. New Year was always a shop holiday and people went first footing. It was then that the older people exchanged presents. Some of the churches held a service as a start to the New Year. It was a time of goodwill and greetings lasted a few days.

Hallowe'en was celebrated by the youth of the area and we went guising, the objective being, I think, to see how much we could get. The older youths played pranks on various people. These they considered innocent fun! I can remember waking up in the middle of the night with the door bell ringing continuously. When my father got up to see what was the matter, it was to find a fence post leaning against the bell.

The occupants of the two houses opposite us had the handles of their doors tied together and therefore they could not get out except by the window, as they had no back door. A crofter might wake up in the morning to find a black horse looking over a fence at him in a shed, whilst his brown horse reposed at another croft a mile away. All accomplished under the cover of darkness!

A friendly vendetta arose between the the older schoolboys and the janitor. They would ring the school bell before midnight at Hallowe'en. In turn the janitor tried various measures to prevent that happening. He would tie up the bell, wrap the clapper in old cloths and on one occasion he greased the rone pipes with car oil. In spite of this hazard, the boys managed to clamber on to the roof and the bell was rung! I think the villagers enjoyed the affair as much as the boys.

A great event for us was going on holiday to my grandmother's in Perthshire. The first part of the journey, to Inverness, took three hours as the train stopped at every small station.

In Lairg, there was a bus to meet every train and a great ploy of ours was to go with the bus driver (called John the Bus) to the night train and watch it coming in and then come back home with him. All for nothing of course.

Although we were very small, I still remember the evening war was declared. My brother and I were sound asleep but woke up to the sound of a bell being rung and a whistle being blown. It turned out to be the local policeman ringing a handbell and blowing his whistle. When everyone enquired what it was about, he told them war had been declared. I expect the majority of adults knew war was imminent anyway. Very few people having a wireless, the only way of communication was by the newspapers and this was a Sunday evening.

In the winter we expected snow and we always seemed to get snowstorms. The roads could be blocked for a few days and the way they were opened was by men with spades and shovels. We always had a good slide, quite often on the road. We didn't appreciate that one could fall and break a leg. On one occasion, I remember the policeman appearing with a bag of coarse salt which he proceeded to sprinkle on the slide.

At that time Lairg had an open-air curling pond and we used to accompany the men when they went to have a game. Maybe we did watch but all I can remember is running around and sliding at the side.

A harsh life perhaps, with few luxuries, but we did manage to have fun.

The Prodigal Visits

Elizabeth J. M. Ross

It was a beautiful morning in early summer which gave the promise of a really hot day. The countryside was looking at its best. The yellow whins ranging along the hillside were in contrast to the verdant valley with its meandering river which tumbled into a rocky gorge a mile or so away.

As Tim strolled slowly along, he admired the beautiful landscape which was very familiar to him. He now lived a nomadic existence but it hadn't always been so. There was a day he could still remember when he had belonged to a well-to-do family and lived in luxury. Unfortunately he had rebelled against the family traditions and had left home at twenty to seek the bright lights but found that the streets were not paved with gold. He had too much pride to admit he had made a mistake and go home; so he got work wherever he could or slept rough and begged.

He knew this area so well; so with a feeling of nostalgia he decided to go and look at his old home. As he made his way through the wood to the kitchen garden the temptation to look through a window became too much for him. He knew the family would be at breakfast as it was still early in the morning; so he crept quietly round the house to the drawing room window. Thirty years had passed since he had been in this room but nothing really had changed. The beautiful softly coloured Persian carpet was the same. The suite in pale green and the curtains to match hadn't changed. He also recognised the inlaid rosewood display cabinet with the collection of priceless china and crystal. The huge mirror over the Adam fireplace gave back the reflection of the solid oak door on the other side of the room.

Only the wallpaper had changed – to a gold colour which emphasised the well polished furniture. He also saw the family portraits and recognised his father's and mother's wedding photograph. His eyes ranged round the room and he saw his brother's and sister's pictures but to his great surprise he also saw his own photograph: one of him as an infant and another of him in his school uniform. This was too much for him and the tears ran down his face. He had imagined that they would have disowned him and put all visible signs of him away. Was this what he had given up to seek the bright lights?

At this point, the door opened and a gentleman came into the room. He had grey hair and was stooped but Tim recognised him as his father. He gazed longingly at the elderly man and perhaps a movement alerted his father as he saw him and came to the window.

'Who are you?' he called.

Tim couldn't speak but turned quietly away. He would go to the kitchen. Maybe the cook would give him something to eat.

Loch Migdale

Lynn Whittington

Two black velvet cows had slipped through the lush green
And softly with their muzzles blew
And made whiskery inspections
Of the cooling surface of the blue glassy lake
Before they started to drink in their reflections

Not a cloud disturbed that sky, and throbbing insect songs
Made the long grass come alive
And the air around it shimmer
As they beat their tiny gossamers to keep themselves a-hovering
Above the still, still lake, attracted by its glimmer

Not a breath of gentle air forced landward from the resting sea
Caused a ripple on the surface,
No active fish
Pursed its lips and rose up to deliver to the sky a scaly kiss
No circled wake, and I began to wish

That here I could remain forever, bathed in sunnied happiness,
Like these summery surroundings
I felt I'd like to stake
A claim to all the solitude and peacefulness and musing
Untouched by this demanding world
Like this sacred lake

Songs – Not of Love

Lynn Whittington

Come away with me, he asked and she said yes
So he took her north to the land where the song was that of
A sky unbroken by concrete, where 24-7 sea was not accompanied
By the demands of the mobile

Where he built a garden for her on the land of his ancestors
Potted stargazers mingling with the heather and the broom
And planted honeysuckle spread through the hazel. Roses and geraniums
Glared against the warm stone of the croft

Where she could sit and read her catalogues to mail order
All that she could not buy here until broadband was installed
Where he could sit and look at her in the warm tones of summer night sky
And plan the future generations for his family

Stay with me, he begged and she said no
For whilst she had slept the city had written the score to her dreams
That sang of promises of lights and availability and late-night shopping
In acres of marbled warmth and plenty

Where crystal clinked, brimming with opulent ruby wine
Or apricoted fizz from expensive French bottles and silver tinkled
Against the feast-laden china on fine white linens, tabled masses
In minimalist style or elegant splendour

It was her song, one which he would never hear

The Bag Lady of Camberwell

Jennie Willans

Bits of this and bits of that,
And a faded silk rose on an old felt hat.
Socks on her hands instead of gloves
Pieces of rag to make a clootie rug.
All sorts of every thing I remember well,
That Old Bag Lady of Camberwell.
She sat on her stool on the village green,
All seasons round she could be seen,
Stabbing at pieces of cloth of many hues
Snippets dropping round her shoes
The toes of the socks cut off so her fingers could move.
The children sat round her as if in a spell,
That Old Bag Lady from Camberwell.
She sat on.
Well into the night when the children were gone.
In the morning she would be back before the sun.
Nobody knew where she went at night,
By morning she would be there and what a sight,
Wrapped in cast-offs from bags and bins
Kept together by safety pins.
One day she wasn't there at all.
Just a clootie rug was all to be seen
Lying stretched out on the village green.
On top was a felt hat with a rose sewn on
And the picture was "Amazing" said every one.
It showed all the children she had ever seen
Playing there on the village green.
Under her stool were some plastic bags
Stuffed chock-a-block with colourful rags.
And to this day the folk that live by that green
Dine out on the story they have to tell,
Of that Old Bag Lady of Camberwell.

Contributors

Jackie Aris lives in Clashmore and is a member of the Sutherland Writers.

Mary Black and her husband Joe live in Rosehall, Sutherland. They are both retired, which gives Mary plenty of time to pursue her writing hobby. She thoroughly enjoys the regular meetings of the Sutherland Writers and the occasional get-togethers with the Northwest group. She has two sons and one daughter and five grandchildren ranging from 13 years up to 25.

Sharon Blackie lives on a 7-acre croft on the shores of Loch Broom outside Ullapool. She is a chartered psychologist, specialising in the use of storytelling and creative writing techniques in therapy. Sharon is currently completing an online MA in Creative Writing at Manchester Metropolitan University and is working on her first novel.

Irene Brandt escaped from the traffic in the city to live the Green life in the north-west of Scotland. She now uses her chosen home, with its rich geology, archaeology and culture, as inspiration for her writing.

Liz Butler retired from HM Customs & Excise at Heathrow Airport about ten years ago, and she and her family moved up to the Highlands soon after. She has always been interested in writing and for a time wrote short plays for her local radio station.

Charlie Byron, a native of Edinburgh, lives in Rosehall with his wife, Lily. He is a graduate of Edinburgh College of Art and spent much of his working life in screenprinting, design work and sign-writing. Interests tend to stray from politics to graphics with instrumental music vying for attention with fudged-up philosophy and theology, like cooking and washing dishes.

Lily Byron, a retired primary headteacher, lives in Rosehall with her husband, Charlie, whom she met during her student days in Edinburgh. She is thoroughly enjoying her retirement and indulging her interests in writing, reading, painting, singing and learning Gaelic. She is the mother of two children – a girl and a boy – and the grandmother of two little girls.

Kevin Crowe was born in Manchester in 1951 and has had various jobs ranging from factory labourer to HIV/Aids worker. Kevin met Simon in 1990. In 1999, they moved to Durness to open a bookshop and restaurant. In 2005, they became the first gay couple in the Highlands to marry under the Civil Partnership Act.

Wendy Davies grew up in London, where she trained to be a nurse. Being more interested in people than illnesses, she then became a Health Visitor. She values all the hours that she spent talking to people, as it has given her a wealth of ideas for her writing.

George Doull lives in Dornoch and is a member of the Sutherland Writers.

Maureen McCreath Henderson Erskine was born on 31st October 1939. She says of her contribution, 'It was an exercise, as the poem says, but Rabbie was my inspiration'.

As a 'Colonial child', **Ray Forsyth** travelled widely when young. Coming over the border to Scotland at 21, and then to the NW Highlands, she realised she had 'come home'. She has been writing diaries and poems all her life. Her poetry usually arises from a life experience needing to be heard.

Mandy Haggith lives on a coastal woodland croft in Assynt, Sutherland, where she works as a freelance researcher and writer. Essencepress published a collection of her poems, *Letting in Light*, in May 2005. She is currently writing a book about paper. She has a creative writing MPhil, with distinction, from Glasgow University.

Mandy Henderson was born in 1964 and lived in Perth until 1981. After graduating from art college with a degree in Sculpture, she worked in Glasgow developing art projects in depressed areas. She has lived in Ullapool since 1987 and works as an auxiliary in the primary school. She also paints and writes and has two children.

Harold Lane lives in Dornoch and has previously planned sustainable communities. He is now working on Solutions for an Abrupt Climate Change; writing a children's novel, *Back to the Upper Palaeolithic*, and a book of theme-related poems; has a novel partly written on the struggles towards a just society; and is preparing a web site.

Wilma Mackay, originally from Aberdeenshire, has lived in Lochinver for many years. She disagrees with the saying 'East and West shall never meet', because she has high praise for both places. She enjoys writing because it needs a bit of rigour and therefore makes her think and struggle a bit!

W. S. MacKay was born and grew up in Helmsdale, spent some of his childhood in Hamnavoe, Shetland, and started primary school there. He worked at various jobs: fisherman, hairdresser and, for the last twenty years, in the oil industry until retiring last year. He took up writing as a hobby after attending an evening class on creative writing.

Bill MacKenzie works in Dornoch and lives in Brora. He is a contributor to *A Sense of Place*, a collection of new Scottish writing published by Waverley.

After teaching for 27 years in California, **Susan MacKenzie** became an exchange teacher in Benbecula. Now retired, she lives in Ullapool with her husband Ian, a native Gaelic speaker. Besides writing, interests include learning Gaelic, reading, music, gardening, fishing, photography, and visiting her grown children and grandchildren in the USA.

Lynne Mahoney was brought up on the family farm in Bedfordshire. After leaving home she trained as an ambulance technician. In 1991 she moved to Dundee to work in a residential home for the elderly. However, her farming roots came back to haunt her and she now has a small croft near Dornoch.

Judy Maker has loved writing all her life and joining the writers club was a very real pleasure for her. Scotland has been her home for three years and is a wonderful opportunity to explore her potential.

Stephen Marrable was born in Enfield, London and graduated from the University of Life with BA Honours in sarcasm. Reading influences: military history, UK Special Forces, social justice. Writing influences: Paul Foot, Max Hastings, George Monbiot. Hates globalisation and religion, votes Independent or maybe the Tories!

Anne Oien is a retired pharmacist who worked for nearly thirty years in retail in her home city of Glasgow. She moved to Ullapool ten years ago and enjoys living in Wester Ross. Her main interests are gardening and travel, which provide inspiration for her writing.

Elizabeth J. M. Ross was born and brought up in the village of Lairg where she has lived her entire life. She still works in the family shoe-shop which her father started.

Originally from Liverpool, **Lynn Whittington** fell in love with the Highlands after spending many a holiday in and around Dornoch. She moved here to work four years ago with her family: namely two teenagers, their Granddad, three dogs and a cat.

Jennie Willans was born in 1943. She is the mother of two boys and has been married twice. She and her husband emigrated 6 years ago from just outside London to the Highlands and they are now happily settled into retirement.